Environmental Hazards
in the British Isles

Environmental Hazards in the British Isles

A. H. PERRY

Lecturer in Geography, University College Swansea

London
GEORGE ALLEN & UNWIN
Boston   Sydney

First published in 1981

GEORGE ALLEN & UNWIN LTD
40 Museum Street, London WC1A 1LU

British Library Cataloguing in Publication Data

Perry, Allen Howard
  Environmental hazards in the British Isles.
  1. Human ecology – Great Britain
  2. Disasters – Great Britain
  I. Title
  301.31   GF551   80–41250

  ISBN 0–04–910069–6
  ISBN 0–04–910070–X Pbk

Typeset in 10 on 12 point Bembo by Bedford Typesetters Ltd
and printed in Great Britain
by W. & J. Mackay Ltd, Chatham

For My Mother and Father

Preface

Although the amount of time devoted to the study of hazards has increased in recent years on many undergraduate geography and environmental study courses, no analysis of the range of environmental hazards that affect the British Isles has appeared. This volume is designed not only to provide such an analysis but also to suggest a methodology for the study of hazards occurring in these islands. A threefold approach concentrating on the incidence of the hazard, its causes and frequency, and the nature of its impact on both the individual and society at large is employed. Thus the tendency is avoided merely to catalogue past disasters, and work on the expected frequency of hazards and on the risk to society is highlighted. Man's activities and decision-making concerning future water supplies and flood prevention schemes are shaped by extreme events rather than averages; cliff protection and building standards are affected by the way hazards are perceived.

In the mass media environmental hazards frequently make the headlines, are subject to intensive analysis and then quietly forgotten as another hazardous event claims attention. Inevitably the impression is created that we are being subjected with increasing frequency to a great variety of meteorological, hydrological, geophysical and biological hazards. A balanced perspective is needed, replacing exaggerated assessment with rational analysis. A wealth of empirical detail has been presented but, in addition, care has been taken to ensure that the reader is able to synthesise substantial generalisations from the text.

The field of hazard study is not a neat and coherent one. Information is scattered and is often difficult to locate. In addition, the available information about the component parts of the British Isles is incomplete and this has of necessity meant that many distribution maps cover a restricted area, often Great Britain or the United Kingdom. Care has been taken to provide a bibliography consisting of relevant and accessible publications and to avoid the usual academic temptation of justifying every statement with several references.

I have been greatly assisted by the help and encouragement given to me in preparing this book. Professor W. G. V. Balchin, Professor I. Burton, Professor R. Cooke, Professor N. Stephens, Dr D. Harding, Dr L. Musk, and Dr D. Parker read parts of the manuscript and I am grateful to all of them for their patience and advice. Miss K. Bradshaw and Miss L. Johns gave me access to their unpublished work. Professor J. Oliver and Mrs S. Leivesley provided stimulating discussion. Mr Roger Jones gave constant advice and encouragement in all stages of production of the work. Above all, my wife, Vivien, cheerfully put up with a hazard–obsessed husband and deserves particular thanks.

A. H. PERRY
May 1980

Contents

List of tables

Acknowledgements

In the preparation of a book of this nature, illustrative material is invariably drawn from a wide range of sources. While every possible attempt has been made to contact copyright holders, I would like to apologise in advance for any inadvertent use of original material. I would like to thank the following organisations and individuals for permission to reproduce illustrations:

R. W. Kates (1.2); H. H. Lamb and Associated Book Publishers (2.2); Commercial Union Insurance Company (2.3); the Director, Building Research Station (2.6, 2.7, 2.9, 2.13); Figures 2.8 and 8.2 reprinted by permission from *Nature*; 2.8, vol. 197, pp. 655, 656, Copyright ©1963 Macmillan Journals Limited; Terence Meaden (2.14); Figures 3.2, 3.3, 3.7, 3.8, 4.2, 4.6, 4.7, 5.2 and 5.6 reproduced with permission of the Controller of Her Majesty's Stationery Office, Crown Copyright reserved; Royal Meteorological Society (3.6); *Western Mail & Echo*, Cardiff (3.9, 3.10); Figure 3.11 adapted from the *Geographical Review*, vol. 57, 1967, with the permission of the American Geographical Society; Figure 3.12 first appeared in *New Scientist*, London, the weekly review of science and technology, 19 January 1978; J. E. Thornes (3.13); David & Charles (4.3); Avon Rubber Company and Greater London Council (4.4); the Editor, *Journal of the Institute of Water Engineers and Scientists* (4.8); R. Ward (4.9); Greater London Council (4.12); Dennis Parker (4.13, 4.14); The Editor, *Proceedings of the Royal Society* (5.3); Institute of British Geographers (5.4); the Director, Road Research Laboratory (6.2); The Readers Digest Association Ltd (6.3); P. J. Lawther (7.1); The Editor, *The Observer* (7.4); Advisory Commission on Oil Pollution of the Sea and the Editor, *The Guardian* (7.5); the Editor, *The Sunday Times* and the Editor, *The Observer* (7.6); the Editor, *Environmental Pollution* (7.7); Institute of Geological Sciences, London (8.1); Figure 8.3 reproduced from *Catastrophe – the violent Earth* (T. Waltham) with the permission of Macmillan, London and Basingstoke; N. Stephens (8.4, 8.5); M. A. Cruikshank (8.6); M. Clarke and *The Geographical Magazine*, London (8.9); S. Nortcliff (8.12); R. H. Osborne (8.13); Figure 9.1 reproduced by permission from *Annals of the Association of American Geographers*, vol. 61, 1971, p. 645, Fig. 7, J. M. Hunter and J. C. Young; Institute of British Geographers (10.1); Figure 10.2 reproduced from *The geography of pollution: a study of Greater Manchester* with the permission of C. M. Wood and Manchester University Press; Figure 10.3 reproduced from *Hazard control policy in Britain* (J. C. Chicken) with the permission of Pergamon Press.

1 *Some perspectives on environmental hazard research*

Introduction

Hazards are threats to humans and what they value: life, well-being, material goods and environment. Because society has learnt from experience and prepared itself to cope with repetitions, the British Isles cannot be classified as a disaster-prone part of the planet although there are numerous cases of natural hazards occurring which have produced disaster situations. A systematic and quantitative world-view of exposure to a series of hazards (Münchener Ruck 1978) reveals that tropical Third World countries are more at risk. However, a highly urbanised industrialised society within a a specialised economy such as is found in the British Isles may well suffer in material terms much greater damage to buildings, industry and complex communications systems than a subsistence agricultural area in a developing country.

A tradition of hazard research can be traced back for over half a century in the United States to the basic theoretical work of Barrows (1923) on how Man can structure and adjust to his environment. Barrows showed that Man exists in an essentially ecological relationship with his environment and is able to insulate himself from environmental threats that are stochastic and discontinuous by a variety of culturally derived processes. Subsequent research involved a pioneering series of studies of United States' flood problems beginning in the 1940s, and during the past decade the development of a behavioural science methodology has allowed the assessment of a wide range of hazards not only in North America but also in contrasting cultural settings under the auspices of the International Geography Union's commission on Man and the Environment (White 1974). Research into hazards in the British Isles has developed more recently, has been more fragmentary and diffused through a range of research groups than is the case in the USA. In particular, work on the magnitude, causes and frequencies of hazards has been undertaken by workers trained in the natural and physical sciences, while quite separately, studies of the management policies adopted to counteract the effect of different hazards has been analysed by social scientists. An attitude has lingered on that the British landscape is somehow protected by divine providence and moderate rainfall from calamities. Although some research papers, for example Balchin (1976), have examined the range of natural hazards experienced in the British Isles, no comprehensive synthesis of existing knowledge has been attempted hitherto. The British Isles are not immune to hazards because every parameter of the biosphere is subject to seasonal, annual or secular fluctuations, and constitutes a hazard to Man to the extent that his adjustments to the frequency, magnitude or timing of its extremes are based on imperfect knowledge.

Hazard research has emerged as a recognisable subarea of geographical inquiry and an important element of the Man–environment relationship that is central to geographical studies. Stimulating opportunities exist for integrating established but divergent aspects of physical and human geography. Hewitt and Burton (1971) have recognised that the relationship between Man and his environment has its positive results (resources and commodities) and its negative results (hazards and damage). The variability and complexity in natural and human systems can make some phenomena, for example a river, both a hazard and a resource. Hazards have been defined by Gardiner (1977) as 'events, objects, processes and substances that are perceived to cause more damage to, or impose more costs on, society than the benefits they give'. Research has particularly focused on natural hazards defined by Burton and Kates (1964) as 'those elements of the physical environment harmful to Man and caused by forces extraneous to him', and for the purpose of a symposium in Australia in 1976 as 'those extreme geophysical events greatly exceeding normal human expectation in terms of their magnitude or frequency and causing major human hardship with significant material damage to Man and his works and possible loss of life'. As such, they occur as an interaction between systems of human resource management and systems of geophysical events. By definition then, a hazard is a function both of the physical event itself and of the state of human society, including specifically the adjustment adopted to cope with the hazard and the state of preparedness. Hazard events become hazardous only when harmful interactions occur with populations, activities and wealth, and with the environments that humans value and need.

The extreme geophysical events collectively referred to as natural hazards stand near one end of a spectrum of phenomena ranging from natural to humanly-induced hazards (Fig. 1.1). Natural hazards can be viewed as processes whereby energy is transferred rapidly from the environment to the works of Man, inflicting damage to both life and property. It is not the total amounts of energy released that create natural disasters but energy concentrated and delivered over short-time intervals. In the British Isles it is the rapid movement of air and water or land and the interconnection between these elements when the movement takes place that is responsible for hazardous events. Many natural hazards are intense in their impact but often their predictability is difficult and their onset sudden.

There are a range of hazards which are largely the result of human action, often the result of Man's modification of natural systems, which are transmitted through the natural processes of the environment that have come to be known as environmental hazards. Burton and Kates (1964) have termed these hazards 'quasi-natural'. Pollution in all its forms is a good example of an environmental hazard. In contrast to natural hazards, pollution is man-created; it is to a large extent predictable in its occurrence and its locality, it is rarely sudden, but pervasive or imperceptibly gradual, and largely controllable. Because over time these environmental stresses may cause considerable material damage, impairing health and even leading to loss of life, they are receiving increasing attention (Burton, Kates & White 1978, Kates 1978). A useful working definition of environmental hazards suggested by Kates (1978) is 'the threat potential posed to man or nature by events originating in, or transmitted by, the natural or built environment'. Outside the scope of this book are the social hazards and behavioural pathologies, such as crime, war and terrorism, which are found at the human end of the hazard continuum in Figure 1.1, as are technological disasters

Figure 1.1   The spectrum of hazards.

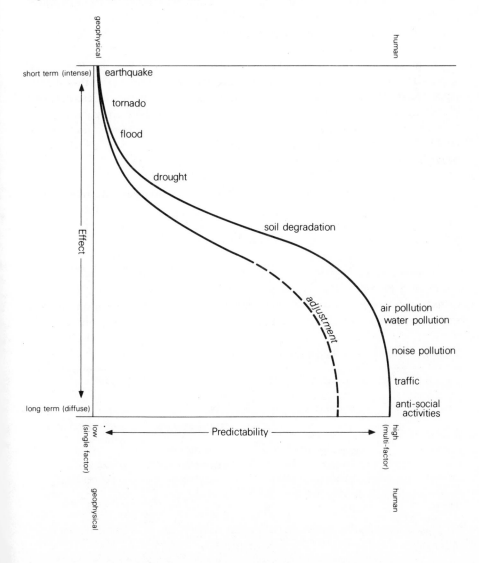

such as road and air crashes. It might be helpful to think of social hazards as intentionally made, while most environmental threats arise from accidental or incidental causes. Care is needed in drawing a distinction between an Act of God and the Acts of Man because as greater control and responsibility for the environment is achieved or assumed, the distinction blurs. The Acts of God of today are often tomorrow's acts of criminal negligence. It is possible to argue about where a particular hazard falls on the spectrum curve and the relative position of one hazard to another. What remains clear from Figure 1.1 is that the predictability, degree of possible adjustments, and the time scale of the effect of hazards at different points on the spectrum varies. In the case of extreme natural events, in several instances the study of these phenomena is a central concern of one or another branch of the natural sciences. Thus hydrologists study floods, biologists floral diseases and geologists or geomorphologists mass–movement processes. Burton and Kates (1964) tabulated hazards based on the natural processes characterised by extreme events and Table 1.1 shows an adapted version of their work.

The arbitrary nature of a broad division of hazards into natural, environmental and social can easily be illustrated by examples. Where should hazards such as cigarette smoking be classified? Such problems highlight the deficiencies of a causal classification and have led some research workers to group hazards in terms of their effects, speed of onset, duration or impact. Hewitt and Burton (1971) have listed some of the characteristics which could be used to classify hazards and these include:

(a)   energy involved, e.g. local level of energy at the damage point or distributed over the damage area;
(b)   areal extent of the damage zone;
(c)   duration or frequency of the damaging event.

Physical and biological scientists emphasise in their studies quite different parameters than does the investigator of hazards. Thus meteorologists' analysis of heavy snowfall commonly relies on the description of the event in terms of snow accumulation and the accompanying wind and temperature conditions. In

Table 1.1   Extreme event by principal causal agent.

GEOPHYSICAL		BIOLOGICAL	
Hydrological and meteorological	*Pedological and geomorphic*	*Floral*	*Faunal*
frost	earthquake	fungal diseases	bacterial and virus
drought	erosion	e.g. Dutch elm	diseases
flood	landslide	disease	e.g. rabies, influenza
fog	soil erosion	infestation	infestation
tornado	mass movements	e.g. weeds	e.g. rabbits
snow			
gales			
thunderstorms			

describing hazards it is the impact of an extreme event, which may be governed by areal extent, speed of onset, duration and many other factors, that is the dimension of greatest significance.

A characteristic of many environmental hazards that makes them particularly amenable to study by geographers is that they do not affect one point location only but have a spatial form within which intensity varies. The acuteness of hazard impact frequently varies over space. Natural hazards are usually spatially confined to a relatively small area of the national territory leaving most people unaffected. Some of the new manmade hazards however, such as nuclear radiation, are much more pervasive. More than ever before, local communities are seeking guidance concerning environmental hazards of all types that should be taken into account in planning for the use of land to be developed. To improve public policy was, undoubtedly, a major aim of the early flood studies in the USA and hazard research programmes in this country can contribute to what O'Riordan (1971) has called the broad tenet of 'environmental harmony'. However, the strategy of communicating the fruits of sound research to public policy-makers requires as much care as does the research itself.

Hazard studies in the British Isles can provide valuable yardsticks both for comparison with those existing in other countries, and for testing proposed models. One of the principal motivations behind research on hazards is a concern for reducing the losses which they inflict upon society. Oliver (1975) points out that in planning for hazard situations it has to be remembered that the urban dweller often has an exaggerated confidence in Man's mastery over nature. Urban populations are often more transient than those in rural areas and have a low awareness of potential hazards. There is a human incapacity to imagine disasters in a familiar environment. Many urban environmental hazards pose a potential threat to the physical and mental health of urban residents, not only in cities in the British Isles but in many other countries, and are being studied by many members of the international community. As Hewitt and Burton (1971) have stated, 'the side effects of our technology are now coming to the forefront as a new class of hazards in their own right'. By concentrating wealth and population, urbanisation undoubtedly increases the damage potential of specific sites.

Existing hazard studies in the British Isles have concentrated on single hazards, individual events or processes, rather than employed the ensemble of hazards at a place approach pioneered by Hewitt and Burton (1971) in Canada. It was apparent, from their pilot study in London, Ontario, that the shift of focus to a range of damaging events would lead to the emergence of relationships and generalisations useful for research and planning purposes. By employing a general hazard ecology a more complete picture of the aggregate spatial distribution of environmental hazards becomes possible. Comparisons of management policies to different hazards reveal whether policy is consistent, or indeed, whether the cognitions of policy-makers differ in relation to different hazards. Suspected inconsistencies and inequities in governmental policies to protect citizens against hazards can be revealed along with unfairness in the provision of compensation or financial assistance to special groups.

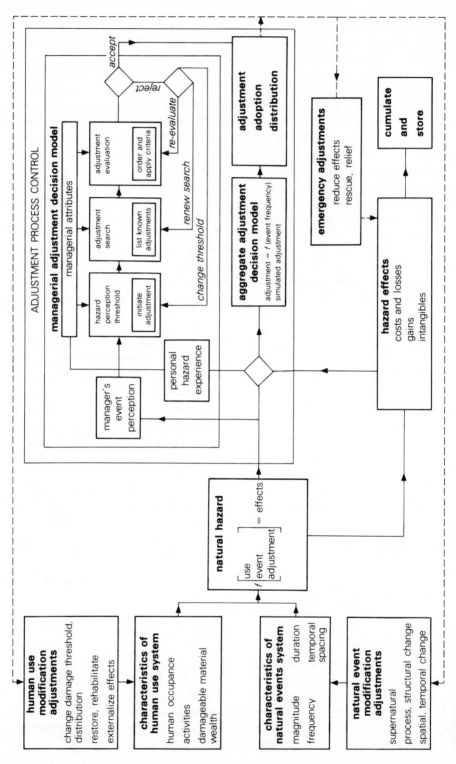

Figure 1.2 A general systems model of response to hazards (after Kates 1970).

Response strategies to hazards

Two kinds of response to environmental stresses, like hazards, have been noted by O'Riordan (1971). Adjustment involves some kind of positive and deliberate reaction usually aimed at reducing the impact of the hazard and may be either technological, involving inputs of 'hardware', or behavioural. Adaptation implies that stress is recognised but in the short term at least is accepted and tolerated.

Important contributions to the analysis of adjustment decisions using a model based on individual resource managers' (e.g. farmers, Water Authorities) perception of hazards, awareness of possible adjustment and evaluation of the suitability of particular adjustments, has been carried out in the United States by White (1961) and Kates (1970). Figure 1.2 shows an outline of a general systems model developed by Kates (1970). Field research has shown that the full range of adjustments is rarely appreciated by those subject to a hazard. There are many factors that enter into the choice of adjustments and the adoption of specific actions or policies. Natural hazard research has focused on perceptions and attitudes especially at the individual level. In future more emphasis seems likely to be given to decisions by groups and at the community level. In dealing with manmade hazards the role of information in the choice process is of particular

Table 1.2 Theoretical range of adjustments to two geophysical events (based on Burton, Kates & White 1968).

Class of adjustment	Flooding	Snowfall
affect the cause	reduce flood flows by land use treatment	—
modify the hazard	control flood flows by reservoir storage channel improvement	reduce impact by snow removal, salting and sanding of highways
modify loss potential	warning systems, emergency evacuation, building design, land use change	forecasting, rescheduling, seasonal adjustment, e.g. snow tyres
adjust to losses:		
spread the losses	public relief, subsidised insurance	public relief, subsidised insurance
plan for losses	insurance and reserve funds	insurance and reserve funds
bear the losses	individual loss-bearing	individual loss-bearing

Table 1.3 Common responses to the uncertainty of natural hazards (Burton & Kates 1964).

Eliminate the hazard		Eliminate the uncertainty	
deny or denigrate its existence	deny or denigrate its recurrence	making it determinate and knowable	transfer uncertainty to a higher power
'It can't happen here'	'Lightning never strikes twice in the same place'	'Floods come every five years'	'It's in the hands of God' 'They are taking care of it'

significance. The study of decision-making and the selection of alternative courses of human behaviour is a burgeoning inter-disciplinary area of research. Kates (1962) has provided a useful summary, particularly of Man's bounded rationality in solving complex problems. A theoretical range of adjustments to two geophysical events – flooding and heavy snowfall, experienced in the British Isles is suggested in Table 1.2. Examples of both the technological and behavioural adjustments are clearly illustrated by these two examples. The task of choosing among alternative means of adjustments is a complex decision-making process which in part will be determined by the response to the uncertainty of natural hazards. In Table 1.3 common responses are suggested.

In the past the identification of environmental risks arose from direct human experience of events, but today the recognition of many hazards depends on scientific inquiry. In dealing with natural hazards, peoples and governments can combine against the common enemy. If the enemy is perceived as lying outside human influence it can act as a unifying force upon society. When the hazard is perceived as the result of other men's actions, even though inadvertent or simply careless, the unifying effect is weaker or may be absent. The policy options that governments consider in relation to manmade hazards are limited, partly because there is hesitation about taking the public into the governments' confidence when manmade hazards are being considered. Recognition that a hazard may exist commonly leads to a series of categories of response by the government:

(1)   When the hazard is first suspected research and investigation is stepped up while a reassuring statement is issued to the public that there is no immediate danger or cause for alarm and that the matter is under surveillance.
(2)   As evidence of the hazard becomes stronger, a warning may be issued that stops short of any regulation.
(3)   A third step is to take action to ban, regulate or restrict the use of dangerous materials, or their release into the environment.

The broad categories of human response to hazard problems in the British Isles can be expressed succinctly under the headings: planning; prevention and warning; and following impact; relief, reconstruction and rehabilitation (Balchin 1976). Central government frequently regards disaster situations as local or regional occurrences falling within the responsibility of local or regional government. Thus a 1975 Home Office circular draws the attention of local authorities to the need to be prepared and to co-ordinate a rapid response in the event of a major accident or natural disaster. Local authority reaction to this and other circulars has been mixed. The more conscientious have by now appointed emergency planning officers and drawn up emergency plans. Some have issued disaster manuals (e.g. Manchester), emergency schemes (e.g. Lewisham) or specialist publications (e.g. the Greater London Council Flood Manual), but many critics maintain that emergency planning remains fragmented. Central government may be pressurised to act by public opinion arising from specific disaster situations. An early example is the Reservoirs Safety Provision Act of

1930 which arose from the Dolgarrog disaster in Snowdonia in 1925 (see p. 80). Other legislation has provided additional elements in the emergent planning structure. Thus the Fire Services Act of 1947 defines the duties of the fire brigade in tackling emergency and disaster situations.

There have been suggestions that a National Disaster Force should be organised to be on hand when required. At present there is a National Voluntary Civil Aid Service which can be deployed when necessary, in addition to the police, fire and ambulance services which are all used to dealing with emergency situations and can adapt quickly to changing circumstances. One important aspect of adjustment to hazards in the United Kingdom is the actual and potential role of voluntary civil organisations. Emergency planning systems can look for assistance from the British Red Cross, the St John Ambulance Brigade and the Women's Royal Voluntary Service, in addition to many church organi-sations of which the Salvation Army is perhaps the best known. The Royal National Lifeboat Institution maintains a sea rescue service and a number of mountain and cave rescue services have been built up. Military forces can be employed in relief and rehabilitation work after a major hazard occurrence. They have specialised equipment and skilled and trained manpower which have helped in national disasters and emergencies. A booklet *Military aid to the civil community* was published by the Ministry of Defence in 1968 to explain more particularly to local authorities about help the armed services could give in the event of natural disasters. The booklet describes how and to whom applications should be made and the financial terms under which aid is provided. Experience accumulates on the consequences of extreme events. People who are trained or experienced in disaster situations do not suffer the same loss in efficiency, and learn to adapt to situations which create anxiety and incompetence in others without such training. Recently a new policy known as MACC – Military Aid to the Civil Community – has been introduced by the services which involves the military much more in normal community life. There is little doubt that in future plans to deal with hazards the military forces will have an important part to play. Specialised equipment such as helicopters, amphibious vehicles, bridging and ferry equipment and field hygiene units is particularly useful. Following severe blizzards in late January 1978 in northeast Scotland, the joint RAF, Navy and Army helicopter rescue teams were vital. On this occasion 17 helicopters logged 305 flying hours, evacuated 18 sick people, carried out 390 checks on isolated farmhouses and delivered 180 bags of food and tons of fodder to starving animals (Perry 1978).

Once the immediate danger is past and evaluation of damage becomes possible, it is usually the financial losses suffered that become of paramount concern. Pressure groups, such as farmers, lobby the government for emergency aid, either through such organisations as the National Farmers' Union or via groupings of local members of parliament. The government sometimes compensates farmers indirectly, for example after serious blizzards in Scotland in 1955, the sheep subsidy was adjusted, although such a course of action may be quite ineffective when losses are high and many crofters with a small number of animals face ruin. Local emergency funds can help to offset losses suffered, and in the case of severe disasters public relief funds may be set up. Unfair anomalies often arise. Hill farmers in Wales claim that while many visiting climbers have been airlifted to hospital free of charge, the cost to them of hiring a helicopter to take fodder to starving sheep stranded in snow can approach £1000.

The Local Government Act of 1972 made special provision for times of emergency and disaster, giving local authorities permission to spend what they consider necessary up to an amount of 2p in the pound of their rating figure for the area. To offset the need for large local rate rises, Exchequer help may also be given. In early 1978 the Environment Secretary promised councils affected by flooding and gale damage along the east coast that the government would pay 75% of any spending that exceeded the product of a penny rate. On several recent occasions parliament has found it necessary to appoint for a short time a minister to take overall responsibility for emergency measures. The Drought Bill of July 1976 is considered in detail on page 109. The same minister, Mr Denis Howell, also took overall charge following severe blizzards in South West England and South Wales in February 1978 and again in February 1979, after heavy snowfall in eastern England. Our membership of the European Economic Community has now provided a further source of emergency funds and it was announced that nearly £1 million of aid would be provided for weather-stricken areas of the UK after the 1977–8 winter. East Anglia and South East England received about £650 000 between them and Scotland £325 000, the money being used for necessary urgent repairs to sea defences and communications.

One important aspect of adjustment to hazards is research into the nature, occurrence, frequency and impact of hazards; and projects on the effects of major disasters in both developed and developing countries have been undertaken in several research centres. A Disaster Research Unit operated for a time at the University of Bradford and personnel from the Unit together with other specialists have now formed the International Disaster Institute, at 85, Marylebone High St, London, W.1. A specialised 'Disaster' library has been compiled and a quarterly international journal *Disaster* devoted to disaster theory and practice is now being published. In addition, aspects of hazard research are found in several other university and polytechnic departments. The response of mature and developed economies to a wide range of natural hazards is likely to prove of value to developing countries seeking to reduce the impact of hazards on their own societies.

Predicting extreme events

Estimates of the frequency of environmental hazards allow a more complete picture of the hazardousness of a place or area to be assembled. Techniques such as extreme value analysis are available to estimate the magnitude and frequencies of natural hazards, and since the results of this work will be referred to frequently in subsequent chapters, it is appropriate that some understanding of the basic methodology is given at this stage. Given a lack of understanding of the relevant variables in human behaviour and the great uncertainty regarding the consequences of human error in times of rapidly changing technology, it is clear that the record of past years cannot provide the same kind of guide to the future in the case of manmade hazards as it does for natural hazards. Risk estimation may be carried out by private insurance companies in order to decide the level at which to set premiums for insurance policies, and recently techniques are being developed (see p. 140) which are allowing regional safety audits to be prepared.

It will be clear from the first section of the book that many extreme meteorological events are associated with hazardous conditions and therefore great importance is attached to the distribution of extreme values. This is typified by the distribution of the set of annual maximum or minimum (if appropriate) values of meteorological elements for a given duration or the distribution of derived related elements such as flood discharge (Gumbel 1942). To illustrate the application of the statistical theory of extreme values it will be helpful to consider an actual example. Assume that an estimate is required of the greatest wind speed in a gust which will be exceeded on average only once in a stated number of years (known as the return period) at Cardington in Bedfordshire. The basic data used for an intensity–frequency analysis is the annual maximum series. In order to extrapolate to the magnitude of rare events, a theoretical frequency curve known as the extreme value distribution is fitted to the observed frequency distribution of annual maxima.

Table 1.4 Annual maximum wind speeds (gusts) at Cardington 1932–54.

Rank (m)	Highest gust (knots)	Year	Plotting position ($p=m/N+1$)	Reduced variate ($y=-\log_e(-\log_e p)$)
1	48	1953	0·042	−1·16
2	51	1950	0·083	−0·91
3	52	1941	0·125	−0·73
4	53	1951	0·167	−0·58
5	54	1952	0·208	−0·45
6	55	1937	0·250	−0·33
7	55	1939	0·292	−0·21
8	56	1942	0·333	−0·09
9	57	1933	0·375	0·02
10	58	1949	0·417	0·13
11	59	1948	0·458	0·25
12	60	1945	0·500	0·37
13	62	1940	0·542	0·49
14	63	1934	0·583	0·62
15	63	1944	0·625	0·75
16	66	1954	0·667	0·90
17	68	1943	0·708	1·06
18	68	1946	0·750	1·25
19	71	1932	0·792	1·46
20	72	1936	0·8333	1·70
21	75	1938	0·875	2·01
22	77	1935	0·917	2·44
23	81	1947	0·958	3·15

Table 1.4 lists the highest gust speeds in knots per hour recorded at Cardington in each of the years from 1932 to 1954 inclusive, arranged in order of size
from smallest to largest. The fourth column contains the corresponding values
of $p=m/(n+1)$ where m is the rank and n is the number of observations, in this
case 23. They provide plotting positions for use on extreme probability graph
paper (known as Gumbel paper) and represent the probabilities that the corresponding values of x (highest gust) will not be exceeded. Extreme probability
graph paper has a linear scale along one axis, usually the vertical, and this is used

Figure 1.3   Return period of highest gust and highest mean hourly wind speed at Cardington,
Bedfordshire.

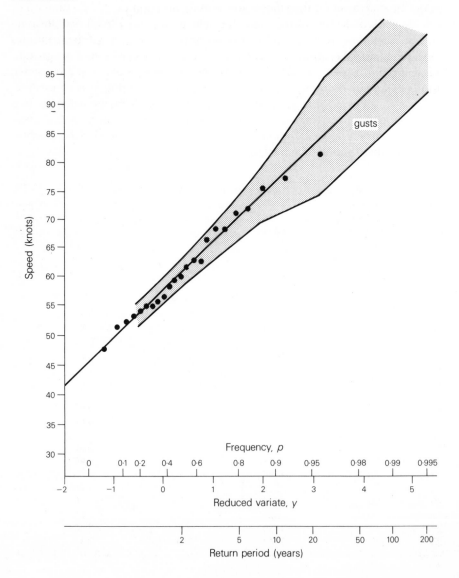

for the observed values. The horizontal axis is the probability scale and is marked according to the formulae $y = -\log_e(-\log_e p)$. The limiting values p_0 and p_1 are never reached but values of y range from $-1 \cdot 933$ for $p = 0 \cdot 001$ to $6 \cdot 907$ for $p = 0 \cdot 999$. If a set of extreme annual wind speeds is fitted to the distribution, then they will lie along a straight line when arranged in order of rank and plotted against $p = m/(n+1)$ on this special paper. If extreme value probability paper is not available, then values of $y = -\log_e(\log_e p)$ can either be computed or taken from published tables. The extremes can then be plotted against y on ordinary graph paper. Values of y for the set of highest gust data from Cardington are given in the last column of Table 1.4 and Figure 1.3 shows the plotted data for both the highest gusts and the highest mean hourly speeds recorded at the station during the years 1932–54 inclusive. Both the p and y scales are shown and also that of T, the return period in years, which is equal to $(1-p)^{-1}$. This is the average time interval between recurrences of an event and is useful because it allows the annual maximum value, which may be expected to be exceeded on the average only once in any desired number of years, to be read off directly from the graph.

On Figure 1.3 the best fit straight lines have been computed and drawn in. The lines on either side are confidence bands which indicate the limits between which each extreme value should lie with a probability of $0 \cdot 68$. An estimate of, for example, a once in 50-year extreme from a series of annual extremes at a single station is subject to an appreciable standard error, which is inversely proportional to the square root of the number of extremes available. By extrapolating the fitted straight line it is possible to predict the return period corresponding to any desired speed, or the speed which has any desired return period. In this example, with less than 30 years of records available, it would probably be unwise to carry the extrapolation very far, and certainly not beyond 100 years.

Extreme value techniques have been widely used in the prediction of flood events and a useful summary of their use in this context is provided by Dunne and Leopold (1978). In the absence of a long reliable data series the only way to reduce the large standard error inherent in an estimate of an extreme of given probability is to call upon neighbouring stations to provide confirmation and to build up a spatially coherent and sensible geographical pattern which will be subject to a smaller standard error than will analyses from individual stations. In the case of meteorological extremes this can readily be done for most lowland areas of the British Isles, but in the data–sparse upland areas the network is often inadequate. A common error in interpreting extreme value analysis is to assume that because an event with a long return period has occurred in the last few years it is most unlikely to recur in the near future. The extreme event can only be foreseen as a probability whose time of occurrence is unknown. In reality it may be equalled or exceeded more than once or not at all, but once is the most probable outcome.

Up to this point discussion has centred on the use of extreme value analysis in point frequency analysis. With some drastic hazards, such as flood or drought, it would be helpful to have data on areal frequency estimation. Unfortunately an analysis of a series of maxima or minima, where each item in the series is the actual average estimated from a point in the area of interest is of questionable value because the complexity of both the climatic parameter patterns and frequency patterns are not considered. In the case of flood estimation the general practice for obtaining an estimate of the volume of water associated with a particular storm over a watershed is to use the largest point value in the watershed in combination with a depth–area relationship. Such a procedure however, has been widely criticised and areal frequency estimation remains a largely unsolved problem.

Bibliography

Balchin, W. G. V. 1976. Adjustments to natural hazards in the UK. *Foresight* **2**, 2–18.

Barrows, H. H. 1923. Geography as human ecology. *Ann. Assoc. Am. Geogrs* **13**, 1–14.

Burton, I. and R. W. Kates 1964. The perception of natural hazards in resource management. *Nat. Res. J.* **3**, 412–21.

Burton, I., R. W. Kates and G. White 1968. *The human ecology of extreme geophysical events.* Natural Hazards Research Working Paper, no. 1. Toronto: Dept of Geography, Univ. of Toronto.

Burton, I., R. W. Kates and G. F. White 1978. *The environment as hazard.* New York: Oxford University Press.

Dunne, T. and L. B. Leopold 1978. *Water in environmental planning.* San Francisco: W. H. Freeman.

Gardiner, J. S. 1977. *Physical geography.* New York: Harper and Row.

Gumbel, E. J. 1942. On the frequency distribution of extreme values in meteorological data. *Bull. Am. Met. Soc.* **23**, 95–105.

Hewitt, K. and I. Burton 1971. *The hazardousness of a place.* Research Publication, no. 6. Toronto: Dept of Geography, Univ. of Toronto.

Kates, R. W. 1962. *Hazard and choice perception in floodplain management.* Research Paper, no. 78. Chicago: Univ. of Chicago.

Kates, R. W. 1970. *Natural hazard in human ecological perspectives: hypothesis and models.* Natural Hazards Research Working Paper, no. 14. Toronto: Dept of Geography, Univ. of Toronto.

Kates, R. W. 1978. *Risk assessment of environmental hazards.* Scope Report 8. New York: John Wiley.

Münchener Ruck 1978. *World map of natural hazards.* Munich, Germany: Münchener Ruckversicherungs Gesellschaft.

Oliver, J. 1975. The significance of natural hazards in a developing area: a case study from North Queensland. *Geography* **60**, 99–110.

O'Riordan, T. 1971. Environmental management. *Progress in Geography* **3**, 175–231.

Perry, A. H. 1978. The response to the climatic hazards of the 1977–8 winter. *J. Meteorol.* **3**, 161–3.

White, G. F. 1961. *Papers on flood problems.* Research Paper, no. 70. Chicago: Dept of Geography, Univ. of Chicago.

White, G. F. 1974. *Natural hazards: local, national and global.* New York: Oxford University Press.

SECTION A   METEOROLOGICAL AND HYDROLOGICAL HAZARDS

Introduction

Although adjectives such as 'equable' are frequently used to describe the British climate, meteorological extremes do occur and they have an immediate impact on a sophisticated economy. Climatic extremes are of two fundamentally different kinds. First there is the short-period, high-amplitude event with a Poisson type statistical distribution while the second is simply an integration of the effect of prolonged or repetitive occurrences of a daily weather situation which in itself is not extreme. An example of the latter is a long run of dry days, any one of these dry days being a normal occurrence but their coherence causing climatic stress. The number of mortalities attributable directly to the weather is highly variable from year to year. Meaden has suggested that in recent years the figures have been as follows: 1975 (26), 1976 (76), 1977 (28), 1978 (26). As medical practitioners and coroners know well, many deaths have several contributory factors, only one of which may be the weather. In addition there are probably hundreds of road accidents annually on slippery, wet or icy roads and in poor visibility in which adverse weather plays a major role. From time to time there occurs a disaster, such as the Lynmouth floods, which remains in the public's mind for years afterwards. Halford (1976) notes that 'there are few catastrophes caused by the weather in other parts of the world which are not mirrored with equal impact by similar events in Britain. Death from cold is as final if it occurs at freezing point or at many degrees below, a collapsed roof is as devastating if achieved with winds of 100 knots or 200 knots, and the filthy invasion of houses by flood water and debris is equally sinister anywhere in the world'.

It is now known that climate is not constant but subject to variations over quite short periods of time. Thus the period from 1940 until about 1970 had significantly colder winters than the preceding 30 years. Lamb (1977) has drawn attention to a remarkable sequence of extremes of one kind and another that have occurred since 1960 and which include: in 1962–3 the coldest winter since 1740; in 1963–4 the driest winter since 1743; in 1968 and 1969 on at least four occasions 24- to 48-hour rainfalls in the lowland districts which exceeded the once in 50 years expectation; in 1974–5 the mildest winter in England since 1834; on 2 January 1976 the great gale which was perhaps the severest since 1703; and for the 16 months prior to August 1976 a drought surpassing anything reported in the available rainfall records since 1727. A full tabulation of the climatic hazards which have beset the British Isles in the years 1968–78 and the deaths and damage that has resulted is shown in Table 2.1. Occasionally there occurs a season in which one hazard event succeeds another in rapid succession. Such a season was the winter of 1977–8 and Figure 2.1 shows the widespread impact of hazardous meteorological events at that time. During the latter stages of the 1975–6 drought and during some snow emergencies it even became necessary for the government to appoint a minister (Mr Denis Howell – Minister for Sport) to take overall charge and co-ordinate action during a crisis situation. The continuing need for ministerial intervention following more blizzards in early 1979 led to press taunts that the country now had a Minister of the Climatically Unexpected. In fact the need for centralised control reflects the increasingly severe impact that extreme weather can have on a complex, technological society, dependent on rapid and efficient communications, although it has to be admitted that political expediency probably also played a part in the appointment.

If the frequency of extreme weather is increasing it is likely that hazardous climatic episodes will also become more frequent. There remains disagreement as to whether variability has increased in recent years. Figure 2.2 shows the number of abnormally hot summer and cold winter months per 30 years. Notice that the period between about 1740 and 1830 has a high incidence of these extremes, and the years since 1960 provide one of the nearer comparisons. Lamb (1977) maintains that at times of meridional atmospheric circulation the surface weather systems advancing east in middle latitudes are largely stopped or blocked, and the resulting stationary patterns

Table 2.1   An 11-year (1968–78) chronology of climatic hazards in the UK inflicting damage of £1 million or more.

Date	*Type of hazard*	*Main impact areas*	*Damage loss estimates*	*Deaths*	*Tentative estimate of return period (yrs)*
15 January 1968	gales	W. Scotland esp. Glasgow	100 000 homes damaged £30 m.	22	
10 July 1968	floods	Devon and Somerset		7	at Bath 10 000 yrs (Rodda 1970)
16 September 1968	floods	Surrey, Kent, Sussex			>200 yrs
13 September 1971, 29 November 1971 and others	fog	Motorways, esp. M6 and M1	(estimate of £12 m. in 1974)	18	
14 August 1975	floods	North London	>£1 m.	1	1000 yrs
1975–6	drought	S.W. England, S. Wales, N. England	>£500 m.		500–1000 yrs
2 January 1976	gales and sea floods	Central and Eastern England	3800 damaged buildings £50–100 m.	28	40 yrs
28 September 1976	flood	Glasgow	>£1 m.		
23–24 February 1977	flood	E. Midlands	£1 m.	3	
12 November 1977	gales and sea floods	N.W. England	>£1 m.	5	
13 January 1978	gales and sea floods	East Coast, Lincs., Kent	>£20 m.	26	50–100 yrs
29 January 1978	snow	N.E. Scotland	cost to Highland Regional Council was £1·3 m.	5	
19 February 1978	snow	S. Wales, S.W. England	£5–10 m.	3	>100 years in places

>=greater than

maintain prolonged warmth or cold, wetness or dryness at different points in middle latitudes. By contrast, Ratcliffe, Weller and Collison (1978) have considered surface temperature and rainfall over the last 100 years on time scales ranging from a pentad (5-day period) to a year and have found no trend towards increased variability of these elements. It might therefore be rash to conclude that the unusual meteorological

Figure 2.1 Hazard events during the 1977–8 winter in the British Isles (after A. H. Perry 1978).

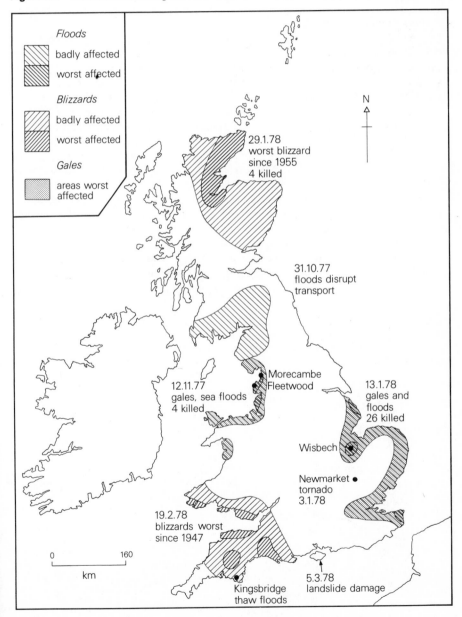

events of recent years are symptomatic of any longer-term climatic change. However, in 1975 one of our leading insurance companies reported that they had paid out almost £50 millions on weather losses in the previous 5 years and began sponsoring a special study of weather variability. The following January, claims reached in excess of £40 millions in one month alone. Such losses emphasise that mankind may adapt to, and cope with, slow, low magnitude, long-term shifts in climate but the ability to cope with changes in the frequency and magnitude of short-lived climatic extremes is considerably less (see Fig. 2.3). Clearly the vulnerability or resilience of the economy to weather changes depends on a multitude of factors, although possibly the most important is the strength of the economy itself.

Each chapter that follows in this section of the book consists of two sections. Firstly there is a magnitude analysis. An account of the incidence of the hazard is given with particular attention paid to extreme examples and to the estimated frequency of occurrence of extreme values. Where appropriate, brief explanations have been included of the meteorological and hydrological conditions which can result in the hazard developing. The second part of each chapter evaluates the hazard in terms of its costs and effects on the community. Stress is laid on examining the adjustments which both individuals and communities make to reduce the impact of the hazard, how successful these are and how they might be improved. Thus it is hoped that each chapter will reflect that climatic hazards are a function of both the physical event itself and the state of preparedness of society.

It needs to be remembered that climatic hazards may not occur singly, frequently compound hazards occur, for example fog and ice together. Occasionally, multiple hazards occur with elements of quite different kinds following one another with damaging force – for instance floods and landslides following a drought – as happened in the autumn of 1976. While the economic consequences of major weather hazards can be substantial, so too are the cumulative effects of less spectacular weather and for an analysis of climate both as a resource and a liability the reader is referred to

Figure 2.2   Number of extreme months by 30-year periods in the British Isles. The lighter line shows the number of months with average temperature over 17·5°C, the broken line shows the months with average temperature below 0·5°C and the bold line gives combined total of both extremes.

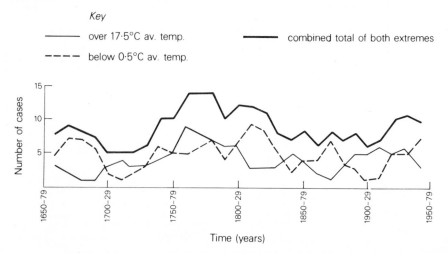

Maunder (1970). The procedure used in the following chapters is based on the analysis of single meteorological and hydrological parameters. Convenience dictates where a hazard involving two media is considered. For example, the removal of top soil by strong winds is considered in Section B along with other pedological hazards although it could equally as well have appeared in Chapter 2.

Figure 2.3 Recent climatic hazards have increased apprehensiveness among householders that they may be under-insured. This sense of unease has been incorporated into this 1979 advertisement for the Commercial Union Insurance Company.

2 Storms

This chapter will be concerned first with strong winds and gales as a hazard and secondly with other types of storms including thunderstorms, hail and tornadoes. Gales are the result of cyclonic storms or depressions with steep pressure gradients passing over or near the British Isles while the other types of storms are principally the result of convective processes in the atmosphere.

Gales

Incidence of the hazard. As Balchin (1976) has noted, 'wind as a natural hazard in the United Kingdom is perhaps less dramatic than flooding, but it has a greater frequency of occurrence and in many ways is more hazardous, as it can strike almost anywhere'. Britain is one of the windiest countries in the world, thanks to its position astride the mid-latitude westerlies. Wind speed may either be measured using an anemograph or autographic wind recorder at an elevation of 10 metres above ground level and expressed in metres per second, knots or miles per hour. Alternatively wind can be estimated on the numerical Beaufort scale which ranges from 0 (calm), through 8 (gale) to 12 (hurricane). The position of anemograph stations in the UK is shown in Figure 2.4. In Table 2.3 the equivalent wind speeds for the higher points on the Beaufort scale are given. In this chapter measured wind speeds will be expressed in knots, but since other literature frequently uses the alternative scales a conversion table has been included (Table 2.2). Continuous instrumental recording of wind speed has been taking place for over 100 years, but in earlier years the number of stations with suitable equipment was very small, e.g. in 1919 there were 14 stations. At the present day there are about 120 anemograph stations in the British Isles.

On average the least windy areas of the British Isles are the inland counties of the East Midlands and South-East England and the windiest are the coastal fringes of Northern Ireland and western and northern Scotland. A day with a gale is defined as one on which the mean wind speed at the standard height of measurement attains a value of 34 knots or more over any period of 10 consecutive minutes during the day. Over the period 1941–70 the annual averages varied from 0·1 at Kew in Surrey to 51·8 at Lerwick in the Shetlands (Shellard 1976). Generally speaking, gales occur on from 20–40 days per annum on northern and western seaboards and between 10 and 20 days on eastern and southern coasts. On a January day the odds against a gale range from over 900 : 1 at Kew to only a little over 3 : 1 at Lerwick. In the windiest individual years there may be more than 70 gales per year in parts of the Hebrides and Northern Isles. During a gale there will be a series of gusts and lulls caused by turbulent eddies. These are likely to be particularly pronounced during rare inland gales, but on the coast the degree of gustiness is normally much less. On occasions severe squalls may occur inland. On 17 December 1952, the wind blew from the west with an average speed of about 26 knots and up to 43 knots in gusts at Cranwell, Lincolnshire, and then suddenly at 6.40 a.m. a squall with gusts of 97 knots occurred. It is the strongest gusts which are responsible for the majority of the damage which occurs, so that the gustiness of the wind is a matter of great importance. Although it is unusual for the mean wind speed to reach force 8 inland in the British Isles, gusts of over 47 knots occur on an average for about 10–15 hours per year at such stations (Meteorological Office 1968). Thus in so far as gusts are concerned there is much less difference between inland and coastal stations than might have been expected from statistics based on mean wind speeds. Wind speeds are influenced by local topography, and strong winds tend to blow even more strongly along a valley if the valley runs in the direction of the wind – the so-called 'funnel effect'.

In Table 2.4 statistics are presented for the highest recorded wind speeds in three geographical locations – upland areas, coastal areas and inland areas. It is apparent that the windiest locations in the British Isles are probably the exposed highland areas in the west and north. At about 700 m in northern England, wind speeds are of the same order of magnitude as over the open sea. The greatest

Table 2.2 Conversion table of units used in wind speed measurements.

Metres per second	Knots	Miles per hour
1	1·9426	2·2
	0·8684	1
17·2	34	

Table 2.3 Equivalent wind speeds for the higher values in the Beaufort Scale of wind force.

Beaufort number	Descriptive title	Speed (knots)	Commonly observed effects of the wind
7	strong	28–33	inconvenience felt when walking against wind
8	gale	34–40	breaks twigs off trees, generally impedes progress
9	strong gale or severe gale	41–47	slight structural damage occurs, people blown over by gusts
10	storm	48–55	trees uprooted, considerable structural damage occurs
11	violent storm	56–63	accompanied by widespread damage
12	hurricane	over 64	widespread, severe damage

Figure 2.4   Position of anemograph stations in the UK.

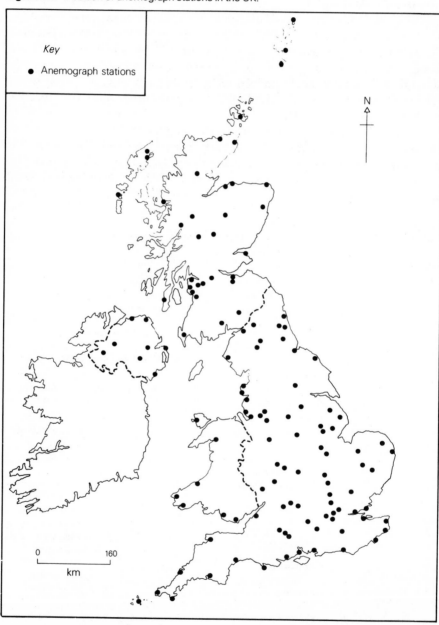

frequency of gales occurs in the period October to February, while severe gales in the spring and summer months are infrequent, although as will be shown the occasional gale in these seasons can be especially hazardous. It is probably true to say that at many locations any month of the year is capable of producing a gale which can set new wind speed records. As confirmation of this, the gale of 29–30 July 1956 produced mean hourly wind speeds of 57 knots and a gust of 81 knots at the Lizard, only a little below the highest values recorded in more than 30 years at this station. The variation from year to year in gale frequency is quite considerable and Harris (1970) has suggested that the years 1934–8 and 1961–5 produced an abnormal number of exceptionally severe gales and to these years can now be added 1976–8.

The majority of the severe gales on record have occurred with intense depressions moving from the Atlantic in an eastward or north-eastward direction across, or along the western seaboard of the British Isles. Gales from directions between south and west result from these weather conditions, veering to north-westerly after the passage of the cold front. Occasionally a depression will achieve its greatest intensity over the North Sea and lead to widespread severe northerly gales, as on 31 January 1953 when gusts exceeded 80 knots in northeast Scotland. Some of the worst gales in southern England develop when small but intense secondary depressions move eastward within the circulation of a large old primary low situated over or to the north of Scotland. Such a situation seems to have been responsible for the storm of 26 November 1703,

Table 2.4 Windspeed data for three types of geographical location.

Station	Latitude (N)	Longitude (W)	Height of anemometer above MSL (metres)	Highest hourly mean speed (knots)	Highest gust speed (knots)
(a) Uplands					
Cairngorm	57 08	3 39	1075	75	124
Great Dun Fell (N. Pennines)	54 41	2 27	857	86	116
Lowther Hill (Lanarkshire)	55 23	3 45	736	86	116
(b) Coastal					
Kirkwall (Orkney)	58 58	2 55	41	74	118
Tiree (Hebrides)	56 30	6 53	24	67	102
Jersey (Channel Isles)	49 12	2 11	98	68	94
Malin Head (Co. Donegal)	55 23	7 24	24		99
Scilly Isles	49 56	6 18	70	66	96
(c) Inland					
Cranwell (Lincs.)	53 02	0 31	68	45	86
Kew (Surrey)	51 28	0 19	28	34	78
Wittering (Cambs.)				52	91

probably the most destructive gale on record which killed about 8000 people and was described by Daniel Defoe. It was this gale which wrecked the Eddystone lighthouse in the English Channel, killing all its occupants. Occasionally in the autumn months, intense depressions which have originated over the western Atlantic from hurricanes reach the British Isles. The most notable example in recent years occurred on 16 September 1961, and led to one of the most severe gales ever experienced over western and northern Ireland.

Since the force exerted by the wind is proportional to the square of its speed, extreme wind speed value data is required by engineers in the design of a range of structures. For these reasons Shellard (1958, 1962) applied the statistical theory of extreme values to all the available annual extreme wind speeds, using the techniques of Gumbel (1954) to obtain estimates of the hourly mean and gust speeds having average return periods of 10, 20, 50 and 100 years at each station for which a sufficiently long record was available. These estimates have been updated by Hardman *et al.* (1973), while Logue (1971) has undertaken similar work using the Irish data. In Figure 2.5 the speeds having recurrence periods of 50 years, i.e. a probability of 0·02% of being exceeded in any one year, are shown for hourly mean wind speed and gust speed. Both maps refer to the estimated wind speed over 'open land country' and it has to be remembered that

Figure 2.5   Hourly mean wind speed and gust speed with recurrence period of 50 years in the UK (after Hardman 1973).

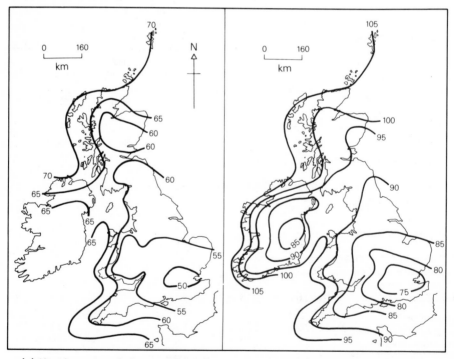

(a) Hourly mean wind speed (knots)   **(b) Gust speed**

wind speeds vary greatly over short distances, due to such factors as topographical channelling, so that it may be necessary to apply corrections to the values shown for a particular site. The range of once in 50-year hourly mean wind speeds at individual stations is from 32 knots at Kew to 72 knots at Lerwick.

If rain falls when the wind is blowing, raindrops will be carried along horizontally at approximately the speed of the wind. Most driving rain in the British Isles is produced in association with frontal passages or passing squally showers, and high-intensity, driving rain is most common in localities in the north and west when both rainfall and wind speed are higher than elsewhere. Exposure gradings defined by a driving rain index have been devised by Lacy (1977) and are based on the product of annual mean rainfall in millimetres and the annual mean windspeed in metres per second. Values of the annual mean of the index range from over 10 m² per second in north and west Scotland, western Ireland and northwest Wales to under 4 m² per second in inland central England.

Maps of the annual mean index with correction factors for altitude, heights of buildings, local topography and aerodynamic roughness have been found useful in assessing the severity of exposure to driving rain and are incorporated in the current British Standards Code of Practice on Thermal Insulation of cavity walls filled with foam.

Engineering works and buildings are subject to structural damage as a result of wind stress. Economic pressures have resulted in a trend towards buildings of light and slender construction, but some modern tall buildings have an unacceptable performance when buffeted by the wind with perceptible motion causing distress and discomfort in the building. Wind loads on structures are conveniently divided into static loads and unsteady (time-dependent) loads (Lee 1978). It was the Tay Bridge disaster of 1879 which claimed 75 lives when part of the bridge collapsed only 18 months after it was opened, plunging a train into the river below, which stimulated the first studies of wind loading on structures. A committee of inquiry found that inadequate allowance for strong winds had been made when the bridge had been designed. As Halford (1976) reports, the designer admitted that he had given no particular thought to the matter beyond accepting in principle the arithmetic done by the Astronomer Royal concerning the proposed design for the Forth Bridge. These calculations showed that although gusts of 40–50 lbs per square ft might occur in a storm they would bear on a limited area of the bridge only. In applying these figures to the design of the Tay Bridge, no allowance was made for the fact that the bridge was a rigid construction with less sway in the wind than the suspension design of the Forth Bridge.

For design purposes the engineer today needs to know the estimated return periods of various wind speeds. The British Standards Institution in its code of practice recommends that calculations of wind loading on structures should use the maps of 3-second gust speeds likely to be exceeded once in 50 years at a height of 10 m above ground level as the major source of data. Wind speeds for design purposes are obtained by multiplying the basic wind speeds by factors for topography, surface roughness, size and height of the structure and for building life. The height of a building is important because in a gale the mean speed at only 52 m over built up areas may be half as much again as the speed at the standard instrumental height of 10 m. Radio transmitter masts and other lattice constructions are particularly susceptible to gale damage. Serious underestimation of the wind loading at the design stage was probably responsible for the collapse of three cooling towers at the Ferrybridge Power station, Yorkshire on 1 November 1965. The gale blowing on this occasion was not exceptional and could be expected to occur on the average at least once in 5 years (Shellard 1967), but the arrangement of the towers caused eddying and turbulence between them and significantly affected the wind loads. In the absence of any contrary information, the towers had been built to resist wind speeds averaged over one minute, but the recommendation of the committee of inquiry set up to investigate the accident recommended designers to obtain Meteorological Office advice as to the probable 10-second mean wind speed with a 50-year return period.

Wind damage to buildings occurs every year during gales, but very little information is available on the numbers of buildings involved, the type of damage, the meteorological conditions which cause it and the total losses incurred. Buller (1977) estimates that on average 230 000 buildings in Britain are damaged by gales each year, involving at least £13 millions in annual repair and replacement costs, plus a death toll which reached 24 in the years 1970–6. Unfortunately, no records of building failure due to the wind are maintained by public authorities or by insurance companies. The only records which exist are reports which appear in local and national newspapers and these were analysed for the period 1962–9 by Menzies (1971) and for the period 1970–6 by Buller (1977). Nearly 85% of the damage reports referred to the months November to March. Minor damage to buildings began at gust speeds as low as 40 knots, although widespread damage occurred when gust speeds reached 65 knots. The most common structure to suffer damage was the domestic dwelling – the commonest type of building – and types of damage included failure of tiled or slated roofs, gable and walls and windows. Generally buildings in southern England were less resistant to the action of the wind than those in northern England and Scotland, and it is clear that higher standards of building regulations have been developed in the north as an adjustment to the greater frequency of strong winds. Many buildings would not have been damaged if they had been designed to withstand wind loads now given in the BS Code of Practice (1970). Current developments in building design and construction are making buildings more susceptible to the wind and are tending to reduce the safety margins that have enabled older buildings to survive. A large proportion of damage to modern structures could be avoided at minimal extra construction cost by a proper appreciation of wind action. The location of widespread damage during the period 1970–6 is shown in Figure 2.6.

Most of the severe damage occurs during a few, often localised gales. For example, the gale of 15 January 1968 in the Glasgow area caused damage to

Figure 2.6 Location of damage to buildings in the UK 1970–6.

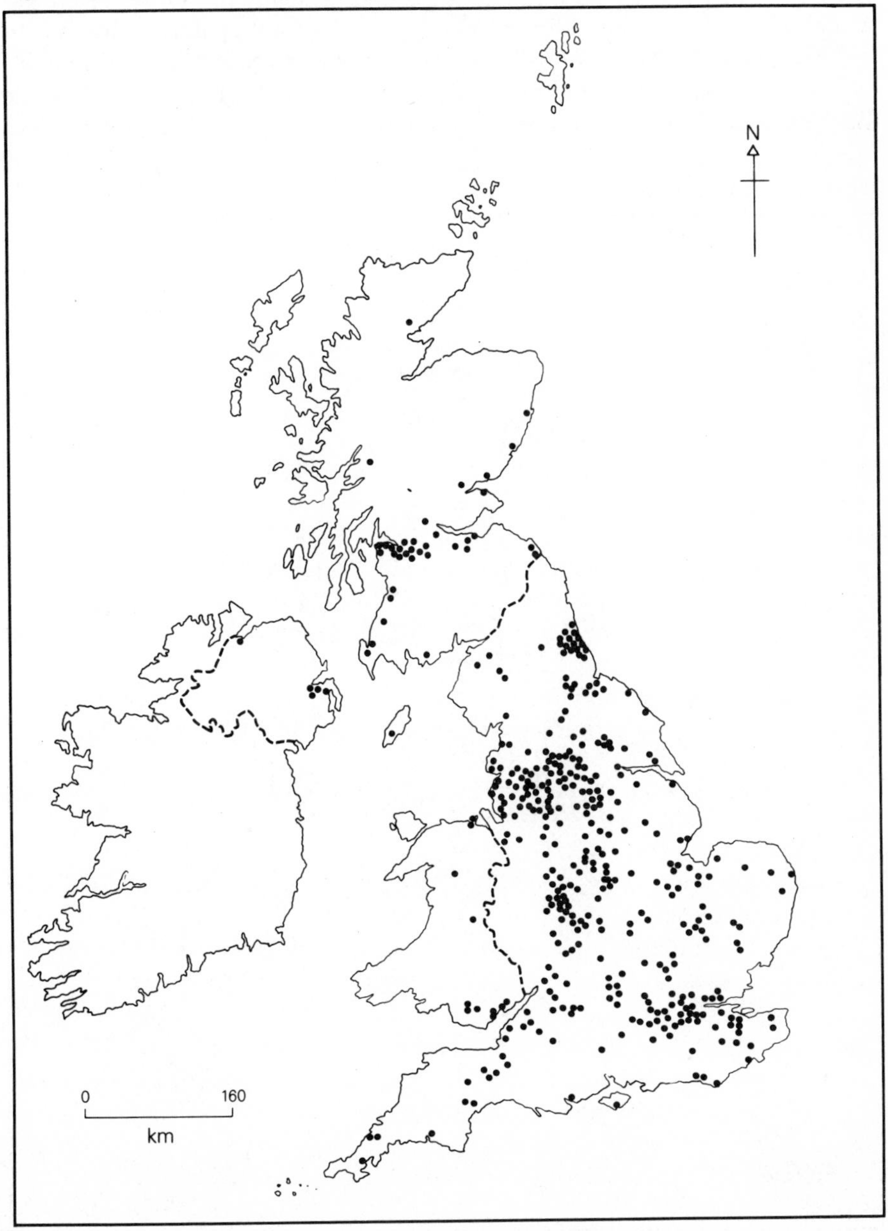

340 000 buildings and the total repair costs exceeded £30 millions. On this occasion there was a need to rehouse 856 people at short notice in the middle of winter and up to 600 troops had to be called in to assist with rehabilitation work. In some cases demolition or complete rebuilding was necessary. Occasionally damage is very widespread across the country. On 2 January 1976, the British Isles were hit by a gale which affected an area probably greater than had any other gale this century, and as Figure 2.7 shows, many parts of England and Wales were affected in addition to large areas in the Republic of Ireland. In Norfolk alone Buller (1977) believes the cost of damage totalled £1·2 million, equivalent to £1·84 per head of population in the county. In the Irish Republic one-tenth of all houses supplied with electricity had prolonged disruption to

Figure 2.7   Gale damage on 2 January 1976.

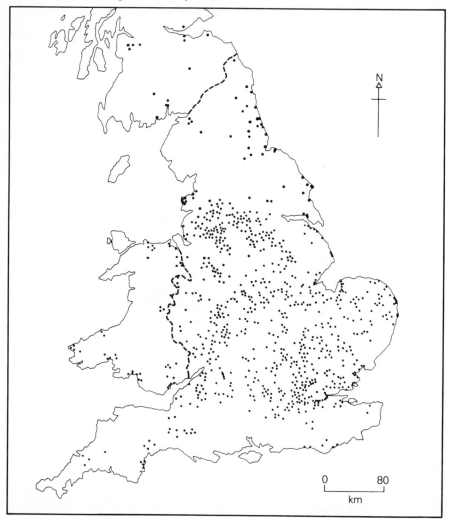

their supply, and repairs cost the Electricity Supply Board £250 000. Local variations in design criteria can lead to a relaxation of standards which can subsequently prove inadequate in certain meteorological conditions. For example, buildings erected in the lee of the Pennines are not usually built to withstand gales to the same extent as buildings constructed near to the exposed west-facing coasts of Lancashire and Cumbria. Nevertheless gales may occasionally actually intensify to the east of upland areas like the Pennines, since deformation of the airflow can give rise to lee wave phenomena (Aanensen & Sawyer 1963). The airflow on the 16 February 1962 is shown in Figure 2.8 together with the mean surface wind speeds over northeast England. As well as a belt of maximum winds close to the Pennines, there is a further belt of lee wave winds some 40 km to the east with a marked line of lighter winds between. On this occasion the strongest winds in the Sheffield area had speeds twice those experienced on the windward side of the Pennines. Winds gusting to 86 knots with a tentatively estimated return period of 150 years, damaged 98 houses beyond repair and damaged about 160 000 others on this occasion in Sheffield. Many of the damaged houses were built on ridges or hilltops, often within the 10 years preceding the storm. The city was declared a disaster area by the government and central government funds were allocated to help to meet the damage bill. The combination of circumstances on this occasion are probably so rare that it is debatable if the odds are significant enough to be considered when laying down local building specifications (see Fig. 2.9). It is possible to make every house resistant to wind speeds such as occurred in Sheffield, but it is hardly economic to do so if the probability of recurrence is very low. Frequently the builder will gamble and leave the owner to 'adjust' to the hazard through insurance. More frequent and thorough inspection of older buildings like churches are needed so that deteriorations of the fabric will be revealed quickly.

Buildings and structures under construction are especially vulnerable to the action of the wind, as are large cranes operating on building sites. Caravans,

Figure 2.8 Airflow in the Sheffield area on 16 February 1962 and the mean surface wind speeds in the area (after Aanensen & Sawyer 1963).

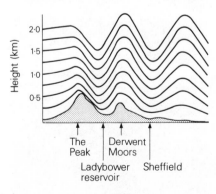

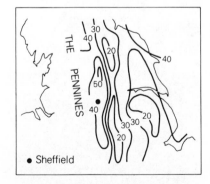

(a) Airflow

(b) Mean surface wind speed (knots)

holiday chalets and mobile homes have become more numerous in recent years and can be overturned or destroyed more easily than many permanent structures. The increased use of caravans as permanent homes means that more will be occupied during the winter high–damage–risk period and guidance is needed on tying them down to prevent overturning. The horticultural industry frequently makes use of plastic tunnel–type greenhouses and these suffered badly in the 2 January 1976 gales in Norfolk and the Vale of Evesham. The penetration of wind–driven rain into buildings is very common, resulting in dampness and, in extreme conditions, the building may become uninhabitable. The worst rain penetration of absorbent structures, built of, for example, brick probably occurs in a relatively few severe storms. Surveys of local authority housing in Scotland showed that one–third of residents living in exposed areas complained of water leakages into their properties.

From Table 2.1 it can be seen that the most severe gales of recent years have resulted in upwards of 20 deaths. Falling or flying debris is frequently responsible for these casualties, and trees falling onto dwellings and cars represent a particular hazard during gales. Many of the dead in the 1976 gale were killed when their cars collided with trees blocking roads. Hoardings are frequently another cause of injury, made the more severe for the reason that they often border pavements.

Figure 2.9 Low pitch aluminium roofs were stripped from these houses at Hatfield, Herts. during a gale in November 1957. Poor construction techniques and inadequate building standards were responsible.

Table 2.5   A summary of wind effect on pedestrians (after Penwarden 1973).

Beaufort number	Effects
6	umbrellas used with difficulty, difficult to walk steadily
7	inconvenience felt when walking
8	generally impedes progress, great difficulty with balance in gusts
9	people blown over by gusts

It is obvious that unless unavoidable, it is best to stay indoors during severe gales. Many people seem completely oblivious to the danger from falling debris. All strong winds result in discomfort for pedestrians, as Table 2.5 shows, and the deaths of two elderly ladies in Portsmouth and Birmingham in 1972, who died of head injuries after being blown off their feet, emphasise that while high winds may be no more than unpleasant for fit, active people, they can be very dangerous for the elderly or infirm. Work by Penwarden (1973) suggests that winds above 40 knots can be dangerous, and architects and town planners should assess the conditions for pedestrians in towns when new developments which can accelerate wind speeds are being considered. Turbulent gusts of wind can be dangerous for walkers and climbers in upland areas, and on occasions people have been blown over gullies or off exposed ridges.

On the roads, cyclists and light vehicles such as invalid carriages can be blown into the path of other traffic and large traffic signs may be blown on to the carriageway. On major roads, and especially on motorways, cross-winds can be hazardous for high-sided vehicles such as furniture vans, and on exposed bridges like the Severn Bridge it is the practice to close the bridge to such traffic. Price (1971) found that between 1966 and 1968 in Yorkshire, 37 vehicles were overturned, 20 struck safety fences and 70 motorcycles were involved in accidents in which wind played a major factor. On the Forth road bridge, if the wind is greater than 27 knots, 'strong wind' signs are lit up and restrictions imposed on high-sided vehicles and cars towing caravans. Such vehicles are doubled up alongside heavier vehicles to act as wind breaks. A vehicle emerging from a tunnel, cutting or bridge which is then suddenly hit by a strong sidewind is particularly susceptible to wind.

The wind has a direct effect on both the reliability and safety of railway operations. Lightweight trains could be overturned or derailed by extreme wind gusts and to ensure that the probability of such an accident occurring is extremely low, a knowledge of the aerodynamic characteristics of the train and the effects of cuttings and embankments on the wind field have to be examined. Most inter-city electric trains draw their power from an overhead contact wire, and catenary system. Strong cross-winds can affect current collection and performance, while in extreme cases, the contact wire may be blown sideways over the end of the train pantograph causing substantial damage to the wire system or the pantograph. Wind statistics and experimental measurement of wind-flow over embankments, together with operational experience are combined to predict local design wind speeds along a route so as to produce a reliable yet economic design. Severe gales may disrupt signalling and be hazardous to train operations. On 2 January 1976, the driver and second man of a diesel locomotive were killed when they crashed into the back of a stationary parcels train near Worcester. Aircraft can be damaged by squalls, for example in December 1974 when a gust of 78 knots was recorded at Kew, one large aircraft at Heathrow was lifted and blown into another parked nearby. In the three years 1975–7 warnings of severe inland gales were broadcast on 93 occasions in the form of flash weather messages. These messages are effectively warnings of the actual occurrence of weather conditions which might cause considerable inconvenience to a large number of people.

Wind damage to crops and vegetation can be severe in the British Isles. Wind effectively excludes commercial tree-growing from the exposed western coasts where the salt content of the air accentuates its effect. Tatter flags are now used to estimate the effect of exposure prior to planting. The gales at the end of January 1953 blew down about 5% of the total standing value of coniferous timber in the UK (Anderson 1954), while in 1968, gales in Scotland destroyed 1·6 million cubic metres of timber, which represents twice the annual cut for the whole of Scotland. Around the coasts it is the indirect effect of air in rapid motion whipping up rough seas, that can cause damage and loss of life. Many seaside piers are now over 100 years old and during the 1977–8 winter, gales destroyed those at Margate, Skegness and Hunstanton and severely damaged several in North-West England. Severe onshore gales can cause huge waves to batter sea defences. Around much of the west coast where the largest damaging waves can occur, much of the coastline consists of cliffs, but in areas of low-lying coasts, as on the Lancashire coast, severe gale damage can occur. On the south coast, east-facing villages sited near sea level have suffered most. Low-lying parts of the Isle of Portland were badly affected by waves estimated at 15 m in height in mid-February 1979 and similar flooding and damage affected Portland in 1942. These giant seas demolished property, smashed cars and led to flooding. Families were evacuated from their homes and for a time all communication links with the mainland were broken. As with damage caused by other meteorological hazards, the government announced that it would be prepared to grant aid to the Council at the rate of 75% of any expenditure in excess of the product of a one pence rate. The considerable destruction at the South Devon villages of Torcross and Beesands during south-easterly gales in early January 1979 by waves of similar dimensions to those at Portland represents a further example of damage resulting from violent winds with a considerable 'fetch'. On other occasions huge waves crashing over promenades have swept away pedestrians and even cars, causing fatalities. At sea, ships may get into trouble particularly if cargo shifts, if engine rooms are flooded or if steering gear is damaged. Once a ship is drifting without power in inclement conditions there is often little that can be done to rescue her. Britain's coasts are littered with shipwrecks and it was this problem which led to the setting up of a meteorological service, when Admiral Fitzroy became chief meteorologist at the Board of

Trade in 1854. The actions of the Royal National Lifeboat Institution and the use of aircraft and helicopters in inshore waters have helped to reduce the toll of lives from merchant ships in trouble in coastal waters, but increasing numbers of 'weekend sailors' and yachtsmen, some of them with very little experience, are prone to danger during periods of stormy weather especially in summer. The biggest disaster in the history of ocean racing occurred during the Fastnet yacht race in mid–August 1979. A severe gale caused 23 out of the 306 competing yachts to be sunk or abandoned, and 17 people were drowned. To the novice, even a strong breeze can be hazardous if he does not have the necessary skill and knowledge. Small craft enthusiasts like other groups such as fishermen, have at their disposal the shipping forecasts of the Meteorological Office, broadcast four times a day and including, where necessary, gale warnings. It is often difficult in the time allocated to meet the requirements of yachtsmen when describing a change in the wind gradient across the big sea areas used in the BBC shipping bulletins. For this reason forecasts for inshore waters are designed to give as much detail as possible over the sea up to 12 nautical miles offshore, and are broadcast early every morning and again late at night. However, many small boats do not have radio, and it is clear that many people who go sailing do not

Figure 2.10   The incidence of damaging hailstorms in the UK.

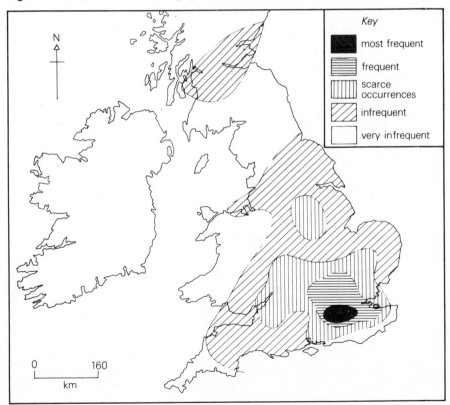

bother to check on weather conditions, before deciding whether to set off. Local radio stations such as Radio Solent and Radio Brighton have also introduced an extensive weather service for amateur sailors. Further publicity and training courses are needed to raise awareness of the weather hazards among these boating enthusiasts. Small crafts may be torn from their moorings during gales and smashed or sunk.

Convective storms

Hail. Although sometimes severe, convective storms are often highly localised and may cause damage in one area, while a neighbouring area remains quite unaffected. Hailstones are normally less than about 10 mm in diameter and cause little or no damage. Damaging hailstones causing sufficient damage – to growing crops, to glasshouses, or to seriously dent motor cars – for them to be noticed and recorded in newspapers occurred somewhere in Britain on 169 days in the 50 years 1906–55, a little over 3 times a year on average (Rowsell 1956). Frequency was greatest in the London region, where it reached about one occasion per 100 years per 100 square kilometres, with lesser peaks in the northeast Midlands, Severn valley and on lower Clydeside (see Fig. 2.10). In about one year in five in southern England, hailstones with a diameter of 75 mm or more are recorded, associated with exceptionally strong updraughts in thunderstorms. Such giant hailstones only occur during the May to September period, but can cause severe damage. In a storm of this kind on 1 July 1968, in the Cardiff area, violent squally winds drove giant hail against windows, many of which were shattered, as well as perforating plastic rooflights (Stevenson 1969). The West Suffolk storm of July 1946 did so much damage to crops that an appeal fund was launched, while a century earlier in 1846, large hailstones are reported to have smashed 7000 panes of glass in the Houses of Parliament. Bulldozers and mechanical shovels worked for 4 hours to clear a passage for traffic after a severe hailstorm at Tunbridge Wells on 6 August 1956, and on this occasion hops, vegetables and fruit crops were seriously damaged.

Thunderstorms. Thunderstorm activity has been monitored for many years by the Thunderstorm Census Organisation (which began operations in 1924), and then by the Electrical Research Assocation. Figure 2.11 shows the distribution of days on which thunder was heard during the period 1955–64. Meteorological stations note occasions on which thunder is heard and the Cathode Ray Direction Finder Unit at the Meteorological Office monitors thundery weather for 10 minutes in each hour over the whole of the British Isles. The data suggests that over most of southern and central England there are from 1–2 lightning strikes per square kilometre each year. Of course only a very small proportion of such strikes cause damage. The annual average death rate from lightning is about 12 people, although in 1914 31 were killed. The most frequent casualties from lightning include golfers with metal clubs which act as lightning conductors and

Figure 2.11   Distribution of days with thunderstorms 1955–64.

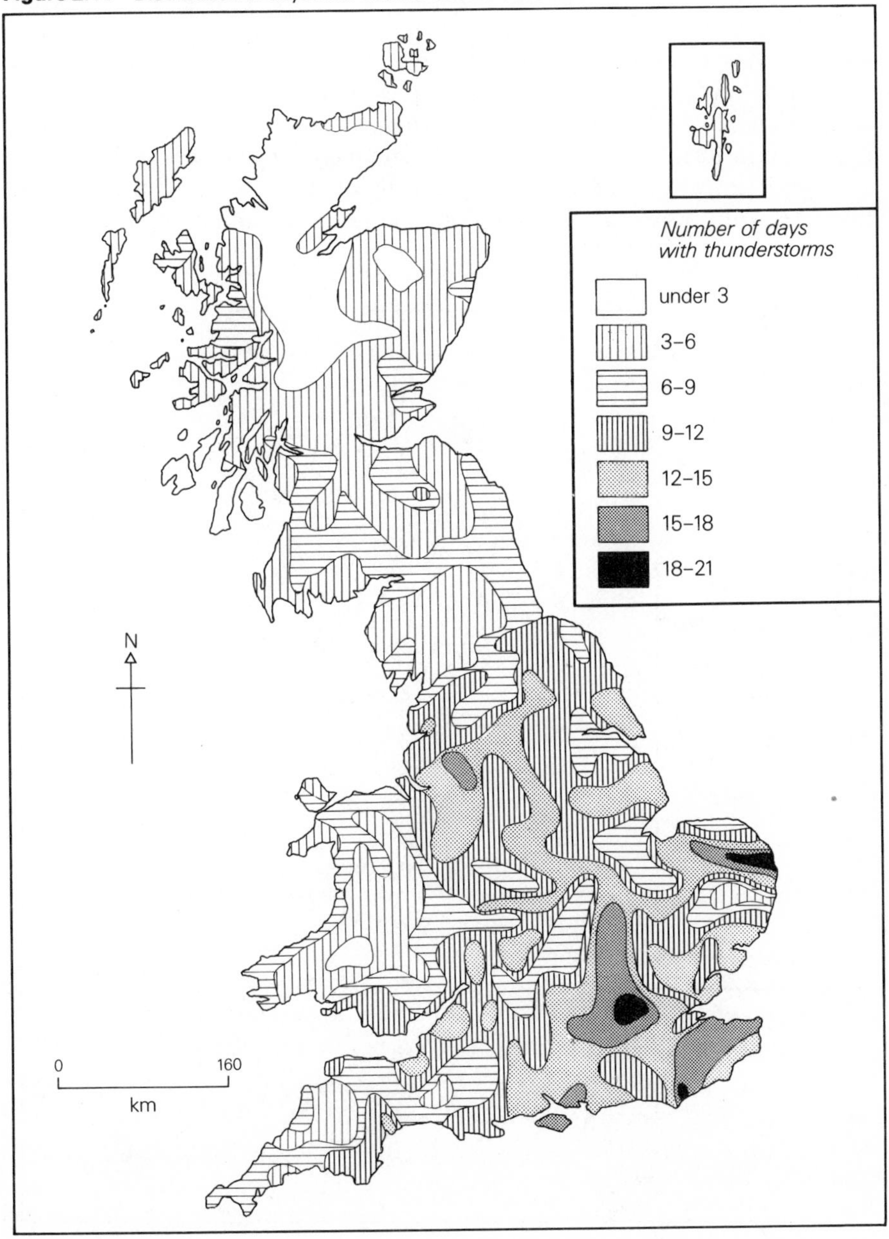

Number of days
with thunderstorms

under 3
3–6
6–9
9–12
12–15
15–18
18–21

N

0   160
km

people outside in open countryside, or sheltering under trees. In the most thundery areas, standing trees that have been killed by lightning are a fairly common sight. A farmer with a scythe, a man fishing and a woman exercising her dog, have been among lightning victims in recent years. Most lightning deaths are single events and do not receive widespread publicity unless the storms are particularly damaging. Lightning strikes to earth can also result in faults developing in the electricity supply system. The risk to property is slight, with the chances of an average individual medium-sized house being struck in any one year being of the order of 1 in 10 000 and even then the damage is generally slight. TV aerials are quite frequently struck and can result in expensive damage to the TV set if the aerial remains connected. An unusual incident happened in July 1955 when 47 people leaning on a metal fence at Ascot races were shocked or injured and two died as lightning earthed. Such an incident provides some justification for breaking the electrical continuity of long metal

Figure 2.12   Distribution of thunder and damage on 22 July 1951.

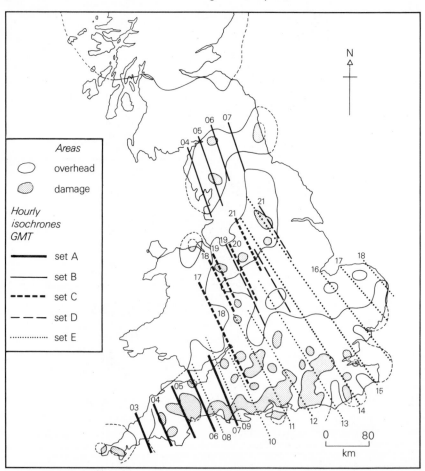

fences. Aircraft in flight have on occasions been damaged by lightning, and in April 1979 eleven soccer players were hit by a flash of lightning at Caerleon, Gwent, one of whom was critically ill in hospital afterwards.

Severe and widespread thunderstorms show a pronounced maximum frequency in the area which is enclosed roughly between the Wash, the Severn and the Thames estuaries (Crossley & Lofthouse 1964) and occur mostly between May and August. The causes of severe storms are instability through a deep layer of the atmosphere, together with strong surface heating. These conditions are most common with slow moving cold fronts or troughs, or with low pressure over the Bay of Biscay or northern France. Storms mostly develop locally or originate over Europe and drift northwards, often during the night time. Figure 2.12 shows an occasion when overhead thunder affected 46% of England and Wales and damage occurred in a wide belt across the southern half of England, as a series of storms, indicated by isochrones, travelled across the country.

Tornadoes. Tornadoes, the most violent and localised type of storm, occur from time to time in Britain, although they are usually less intense and destructive than the fully developed storms that affect the Prairie states of North America. The tornado is an intense whirl of small diameter, with a reduction of pressure of 100–300 mb within a few metres of the centre and with wind speeds that may exceed 200 knots. Many examples have been described from different parts of the country. Among historical examples, the Devon tornado of October 1638 which destroyed Widecombe church, is among the best known. In recent times severe damage occurred on 21 May 1950 when three tornadoes affected the district between Buckingham and Norfolk (Lamb 1957), the Acton area of West London was affected on 8 December 1954, and there was considerable damage to buildings along a track from the Isle of Wight to Upminster in Essex from tornadoes on 25 January 1971. Typically damage to buildings is extremely localised, often displaying a linear pattern, with destruction affecting a path that may be as little as 10–30 m wide and rarely exceeding 150 m (see Fig. 2.13). Apart from damage caused by severe vertical and horizontal air currents, damage of an explosive type may occur when a tornado passes close to buildings, due to the much reduced air pressure in the middle of the tornado. Walls and windows may burst outwards, severely damaging buildings, and roofs can also be sucked off.

Recorded tornadoes have occurred within the circulation of a depression frequently centred just to the west of the British Isles in regions where light winds and much stronger winds were in close juxtaposition, for example, at the tip of the elongated trough. Prerequisites for tornadoes are warm moist air at the surface underlying cold dry air aloft, giving conditions of potential instability and leading to strong persistent vertical currents. Tornado events in Britain are now monitored by TORRO (The Tornado and Storm Research Organisation) and their intensity can be described by means of the scale shown in Table 2.6. Studies of the incidence and strength of tornadoes suggest they are much more

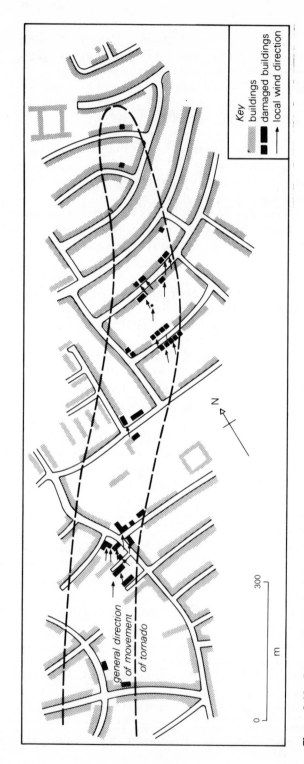

Figure 2.13 Damage by tornado in Welling, Kent.

frequent than is often realised (78 occurred in the years 1963–6) with a maximum frequency in the May to July period and a minimum frequency in late winter and early spring (Meaden 1976). Sometimes in winter several tornadoes develop on the same day, usually as a marked cold front moves eastward across the country. For example TORRO noted more than 10 tornadoes in eastern England on 3 January 1978, the most serious of which damaged racing stables, buildings and cars in Newmarket and probably rated Force 5 on the TORRO scale shown in Table 2.6. The region with the greatest frequency of the more powerful tornadoes stretches from the north Midlands southeastwards to Kent, while no severe tornadoes have been reported from Scotland, northern England or West Wales (see Fig. 2.14). Meaden has suggested that at least 12 tornadoes recorded in Britain have reached force 6–8 on the scale. Water spouts are similar to tornadoes, but they form over the sea. They are observed quite frequently in coastal waters around the British Isles and have caused damage to harbours and boats on several occasions.

Table 2.6 The TORRO tornado intensity scale.

Force	Name	Characteristic damage
FC	funnel cloud or incipient tornado	No damage to structures. No damage in the country except possibly agitation to highest tree tops.
0	light tornado	(a) Loose, light litter raised from the ground in spirals. (b) Temporary structures like marquees seriously affected. (c) Slight dislodging of the least secure and most exposed tiles and slates. (d) Some twigs snapped off trees. Bushes may be damaged.
1	mild tornado	(a) Planks, deckchairs, light garden furniture levitated. (b) Minor to major damage to sheds, outhouses, and other wooden structures. (c) Some dislodging of tiles, slates and chimney pots. (d) Hayricks seriously disarranged. Damage to shrubs and trees.
2	moderate tornado	(a) Exposed, heavy mobile homes displaced, light caravans damaged. (b) Minor to major damage to sheds, lock-up garages etc. (c) Considerable damage to slates, tiles and chimney stacks. (d) Big branches of trees torn off, tornado track easily followed by damage to crops, trees etc.

Force	Name	Characteristic damage
3	strong tornado	(a) Mobile homes displaced, damaged or overturned, caravans badly damaged. (b) Sheds and outbuildings torn from supports and foundations. (c) Severe roof damage to houses. (d) Considerable damage to strong trees.
4	severe tornado	(a) Caravans and mobile homes destroyed or gravely damaged. (c) Entire roofs torn off some wooden houses and light industrial buildings. (d) Large, well-rooted trees uprooted, snapped or twisted apart.
5	intense tornado	(c) Extensive failure of roofs. Small weak buildings may collapse. (d) Trees carried through the air.
6	moderately devastating tornado	(a) Motor vehicles over 1 ton lifted off ground. (c) Most residences lose roofs and some also lose walls.
7	strongly devastating tornado	(c) Walls of wooden houses and buildings torn away. Some walls of stone or brickhouses collapse. Trains de-railed.
8	severely devastating tornado	(c) Entire frame houses levelled, most other houses collapse in part or whole.
9	very severely devastating tornado	(c) Many steel structures badly damaged. Trains hurled some distance.
10	intensely devastating tornado	(c) Entire frame and wooden houses hurled from foundations.
11	very intensely devastating tornado	(c) Steel-reinforced concrete buildings severely damaged.
12	super tornadoes	

Subdivisions (a), (b) and (c) apply broadly to urban situations while (d) applies to rural situations.

Conclusions

Most kinds of storms are high intensity but often short duration phenomena. The wind hazard results from both the direct and indirect effects of air in motion. Direct damage may be caused to structures by extreme gusts which exceed the damage threshold, and wind damage represents a major component of property damage in the British Isles. The incidence of severe convective storms is rather capricious and hence difficult to forecast accurately, although the general atmospheric instability necessary for such storms to develop can be recognised. More accurate monitoring is revealing that storms with tornado characteristics are more common than had been suspected, although often the damage they cause is extremely localised.

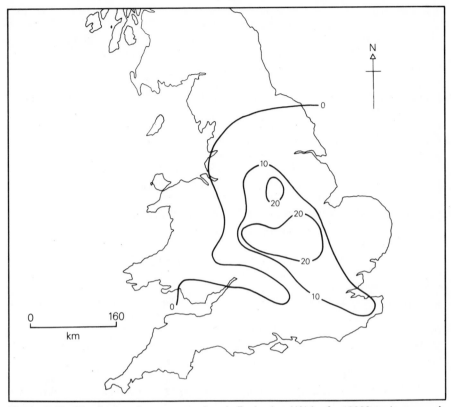

Figure 2.14 Distribution of severe tornadoes in England and Wales for 10000 sq. km areas. A severe tornado is one which reaches or exceeds force 4 on the TORRO scale (after Meaden 1976).

Bibliography

Aanensen, C. J. M. and J. S. Sawyer 1963. The gale of 16 February 1962 in the West Riding of Yorkshire. *Nature* **197**, 654–6.

Anderson, K. F. 1954. Gales and gale damage in forests with particular reference to the effects of the storm of January 1953 in NE Scotland. *Forestry* **27**, 97–121.

Balchin, W. G. V. 1976. Adjustments to natural hazards in the UK. *Foresight* **2**, 2–18.

British Standards Institution 1970. Wind loads. In *BS Code of Practice CP3*. Chapter 5, Part 2. London: BSI.

Buller, P. S. J. 1977. *Gale damage to buildings and structures in the UK 2 January 1976*. Building Research Establishment Current Paper 42/77. Watford, England: BRE.

Crossley, A. F. and N. Lofthouse 1964. The distribution of severe thunderstorms over Great Britain. *Weather* **19**, 172–6.

Gumbel, E. J. 1954. *Statistical theory of extreme values and some practical applications*. Appl. Math. Ser., no. 33. Washington DC: National Bureau of Statistics.

Halford, I. 1976. *British weather disasters*. Newton Abbot: David and Charles.

Hardman, C. E. *et al*. 1973. *Extreme winds over the UK for periods ending 1971*. Climatol. Mem., no. 501. Bracknell, England: Met. Office.

Harris, R. D. 1970. Notable British gales of the past 50 years. *Weather* **25**, 57–68.

Hewitt, K. and I. Burton 1971. *The hazardousness of a place*. Research Publ., no. 6. Toronto: Dept of Geography, Univ. of Toronto.

Lacy, R. E. 1977. *Climate and building in Britain*. London: HMSO.

Lamb, H. H. 1957. *Tornadoes in England 21 May 1950*. Geophys. Mem., no. 99. Bracknell, England: Met. Office.

Lamb, H. H. 1977. *Climate, past, present and future*. vol. 2. London: Methuen.

Lee, B. E. 1978. Extreme wind data and building design. *Weather* **33**, 416–22.

Logue, J. J. 1971. *Extreme wind speeds in Ireland*. Tech. Note. Dublin: Met. Office.

Maunder, W. J. 1970. *The value of the weather*. London: Methuen.

Meaden, G. T. 1976. Tornadoes in Britain, their intensities and distribution in space and time. *J. Meteorol.* **1**, 242–51.

Menzies, J. B. 1971. Wind damage to buildings. *Building* **221**, 67–76.

Meteorological Office 1968. *Tables of surface wind speed and direction over the United Kingdom*. London: HMSO.

Penwarden, A. D. 1973. Acceptable wind speed in towns. *Building Sci.* **8**, 259–67.

Price, B. T. 1971. Airflow problems related to surface transport systems. *Phil. Trans R. Soc. A.* **269**, 327–33.

Ratcliffe, R. A. S., J. Weller and P. Collison 1978. Variability in the frequency of unusual weather over approximately the last century. *Q. J. R. Met. Soc.* **104**, 243–56.

Rowsell, E. H. 1956. Damaging hailstorms. *Meteorol. Mag.* **85**, 344–6.

Shellard, H. C. 1958. Extreme wind speeds over the UK. *Meteorol. Mag.* **87**, 357–65.

Shellard, H. C. 1962. Extreme wind speeds over the UK for periods ending 1959. *Meteorol. Mag.* **91**, 39–47.

Shellard, H. C. 1967. Collapse of cooling towers in a gale at Ferrybridge, 1 November 1965. *Weather* **22**, 232–40.

Shellard, H. C. 1976. Wind. In *The climate of the British Isles*, T. J. Chandler and S. Gregory (eds), 39–73. London: Longman.

Stevenson, C. M. 1969. The dust fall and severe storms of 1 July 1968. *Weather* **24**, 126–32.

3 Snow, frost and cold

'when he says to the snow "fall on the earth", or tells the rain to pour down in torrents he brings all man's strivings to a standstill'

Job 37:6

Introduction

Snow, frost and cold weather occur in most winters, but most frequently constitute a hazard when they occur over protracted periods or during the latter part of the spring when they can severely damage growing crops. Because severe winter weather is relatively infrequent in its occurrence, investment in preventative measures is inadequate to cope with conditions on such occasions. As Manley (1952) says 'over a large part of the British Isles the more impressive extremes of our winter weather occur with somewhat dangerous rarity'. A major impact of the snow hazard is manifested in the disruption of transportation facilities, and even small accumulations can curtail movement and contribute to accidents in a mobile society such as our own. In the most severe winters, of which 1946–7, 1962–3 and 1978–9 provide the most outstanding examples, many aspects of the economy can be affected with consequent heavy financial losses. Disruption resulting from snow and ice, like that resulting from other hazards described in this book, is only partially attributable to the physical properties of the hazard. The adjustments which communities and individuals make to modify the hazard and reduce its impact need to be fully appraised. It needs to be remembered that snow can be a valuable resource, for example for recreation purposes, and has led to the growth of an important skiing industry in Scotland, although in our uplands snow and cold represent a hazard for the unprepared hillwalker and climber. Also on the credit side of the equation, snow can kill off damaging insect pests, while a snowpack may represent an important source of water for reservoir replenishment.

Unlike many other countries which experience adverse winter conditions, Great Britain has no central body which is concerned with all aspects of winter

Table 3.1 Distribution of winters with mean temperature below 3·0°C in 50-year periods between 1728–1977.

1728–1777	17
1778–1827	19
1828–1877	12
1878–1927	10
1928–1977	8

maintenance, including research, development and organisation. It has been suggested that a National Winter Maintenance Organisation could help to reduce the disruption that so frequently accompanies winter weather (Hornigold 1970). Economic studies of the costs to the community of winter conditions at present are conspicuously absent.

Incidence of the hazard

The distribution of cold winters (with a mean temperature in central England below 3·0°C) has varied considerably over the last 250 years as can be seen in Table 3.1. A study of the instrumental and other records of the past few hundred years reveals secular variations in cold winter frequency which are statistically significant, implying that climatic changes have occurred during this period.

The comparative absence of cold winters during the first 40 years of this century is one of the more remarkable features of the distribution and un-doubtedly led to a complacent attitude towards the need to prepare for severe weather. Clearly it would be prudent to take more precautions against frost and snow than was considered necessary before 1940.

Severe winters, like 1962–3, occur when Atlantic depressions are prevented from moving from south-west to north-east on their normal tracks between Scotland and Iceland by the establishment of high pressure in the Greenland–

Figure 3.1   500 mb upper air chart for January 1963.

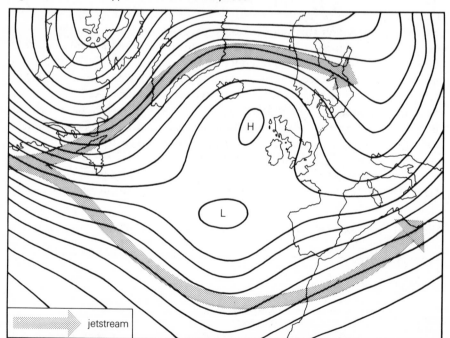

Scandinavia region. Such blocking highs advect very cold air of continental origin over the British Isles, and these bitterly cold air masses are only modified a little in their surface layers by their passage over the North Sea. The 500 mb upper air chart for January 1963 (see Fig. 3.1) gives a good impression of how the normal westerly current aloft which steers the surface depressions, was forced to split by the presence of a blocking high north of the British Isles. During the 1962–3 winter the blocking was unusually persistent and it was the length as well as the severity of the cold spell over the British Isles that was outstanding, lasting in most places from 22 December to 4–6 March. The winter was probably the coldest over most of England and Wales since 1740. Winter cold spells normally result either from the arrival of easterly winds from the Continent, or from northerly winds with a direct trajectory from the Arctic. Long cold spells, such as occurred in 1962–3, are normally made up of a mixture of the 2 types, sometimes with intervening transient periods of slow thaw as mild air from the Atlantic penetrates to some parts of the country.

Figure 3.2   Extreme value analysis of winter temperature in the UK. The mean temperatures are the lowest mean winter temperatures of the decades. Upper curve is for decades 1701–10 to 1951–60 (right hand temperature scale). The lower curve is for decades 1706–15 to 1956–65 (left hand temperature scale).

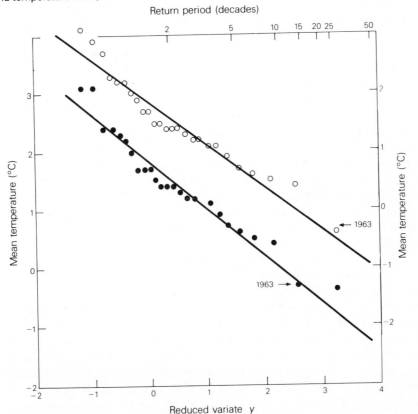

Although we can identify the outward symptoms of such extreme winters, we cannot yet adequately explain why they occur or when they are likely to recur. However, work at the Meteorological Office (e.g. Folland 1975) is continuing into the search for useful predictors of severe winters. It seems that after cool even dated year summers in the UK the following winter has a high probability of being either very mild or very cold and a study of the autumn atmospheric circulation in such years can help in the prediction of the type of winter. A leading contender in explaining why the atmosphere in some winters settles into a pattern of high latitude blocking is the existence of large-scale sea surface temperature anomalies. American workers (Namias 1963) have suggested that anomalous Pacific sea temperatures could have been responsible. Work in the British Meteorological Office has focused attention on the possibility that high sea surface temperatures in the Atlantic off West Africa could have played a major part in maintaining the anomalous atmospheric circulation for more than two months in 1962–3.

After a winter such as 1962–3 it is important to consider whether the event is so exceptional that some special cause for it might have to be sought. A statistical examination of the long series of temperature records available for central England has been carried out by Shellard (1968). Extreme value analysis reveals (Fig. 3.2) a return period of between 150 and 200 years for a winter as severe as that of 1962–3, and it is clear from the graph that the data are reasonably well fitted by a straight line, with the 1963 winter well within the population of other cold winters that have been experienced in this country. Using accumulated temperatures as a measure of winter severity Lyness and Badger (1970) find that the return period of the 1962–3 winter varied from about 90 years in the Midlands to little more than 20 years in Scotland. Some climatologists have claimed to detect an 11–12 year cycle in the frequency of severe winters – 1917, 1929, 1940, 1951 and 1963 all having much below normal temperatures. However, the cycle does not appear to have continued into the 1970s, and despite intensive research efforts, to try to recognise in the characteristics of the autumnal atmospheric circulation, the symptoms of a severe winter it would seem to be prudent to plan on the basis that they come in a quasi-random manner every 10–20 years. We must not fall into the trap of a series of mild winters, such as occurred during the early 1970s, lulling us into a false sense of security.

A recent draft Code of Practice has specified that the once-in-a-120-year extreme temperature should be used in the design of the main structural elements of bridges and similar structures. Some steels used in the construction of masts and pylons are subject to brittle fracture at low temperatures and for these reasons Hopkins and Whyte (1975) have made a study of extreme minimum temperatures. The annual minimum temperature likely to occur once in 50 years at mean sea level is shown in Figure 3.3. It can be seen that values range from below $-20°C$ in several parts of inland Scotland and extreme northern England to about $-6°C$ in the Scilly Isles. In upland areas, freezing conditions may persist night and day for extended periods, and at Moor House, Cumbria

Figure 3.3   Fifty year extreme minimum temperatures in the UK (after Hopkins & Whyte 1975).

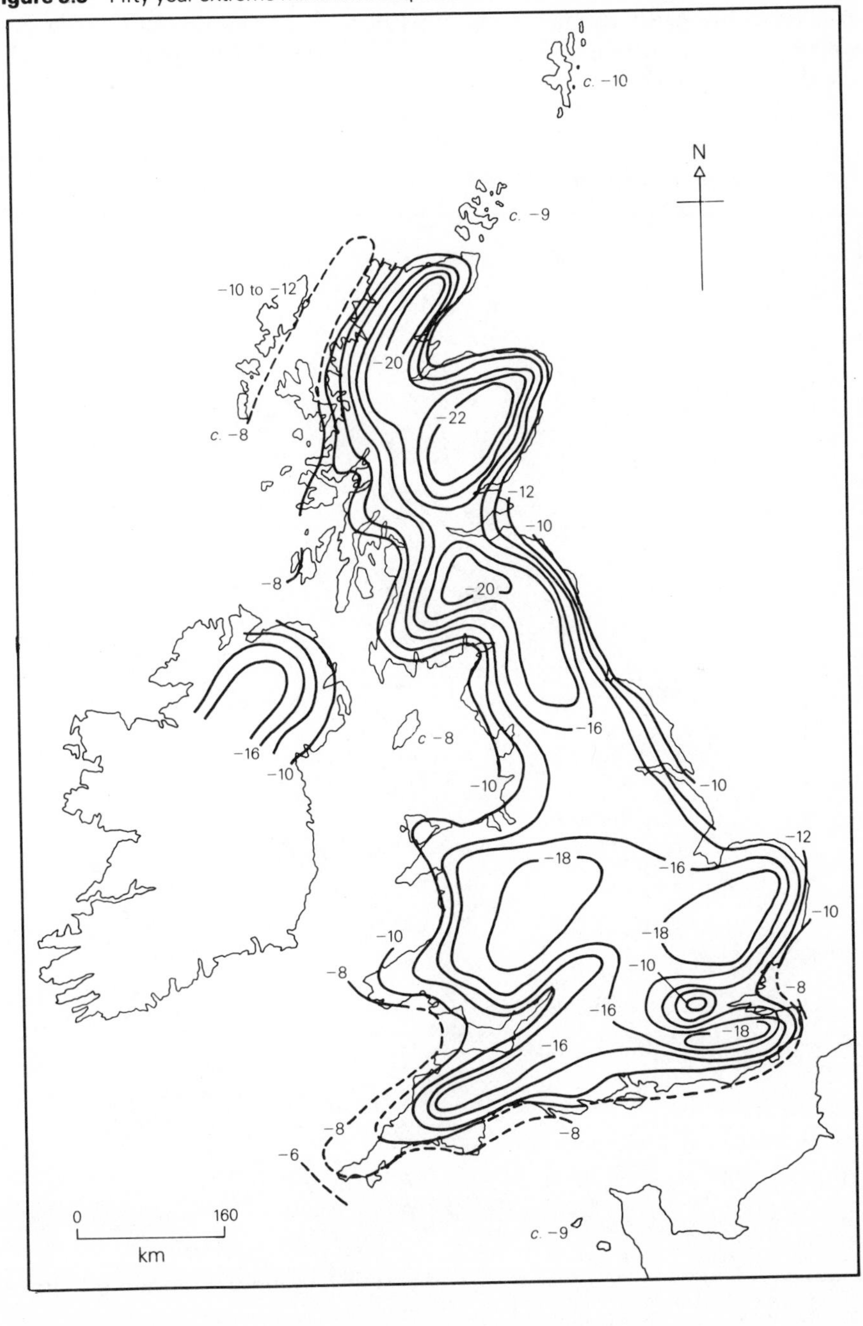

during the 1962–3 winter, temperatures remained below freezing for 34 consecutive days. Even on low ground in the South occasional long freezing spells occur, and Kew noted nine consecutive days in January 1963.

Although less severe, spring radiation frosts can do far more damage than those of winter, because they occur when growing crops are highly susceptible. Air frosts in April and May occur particularly during periods when cold northerly and north-westerly winds affect the British Isles giving clear, calm conditions at night favouring strong radiative cooling. The incidence of frost

Figure 3.4   Snow survey stations 1976–7.

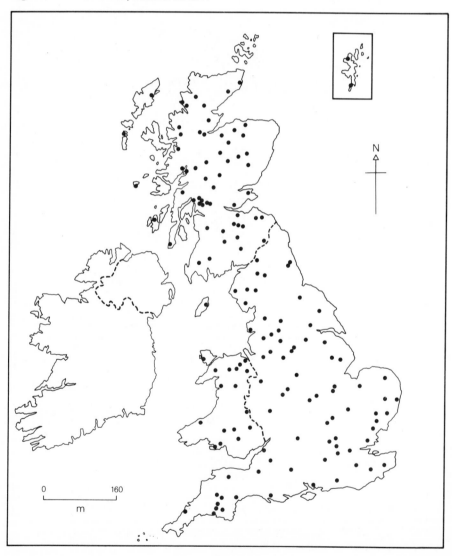

varies in different topographical situations, since cold dense air sinks and flows downhill to accumulate in valley bottoms, where normally the lowest temperatures are recorded. The average date of the year's last air frost varies from the end of February in extreme western Cornwall to the latter half of April over a large area of the Midlands and eastern and southern England. In the North the air frost season extends into May in most districts. Occasionally, a cold night in

Figure 3.5 Mean number of days with snow lying at 09.00 hours each winter. Based on data for the period 1941–70.

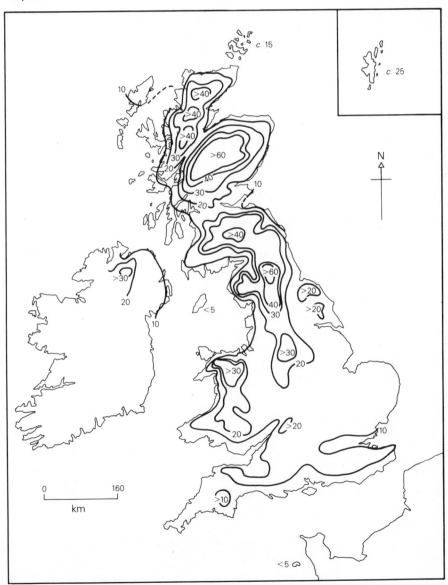

June will produce both ground and air frost; Taylor (1967) instances the night of 22 June 1957 when a killing frost affected the potato crop in Lancashire and one farmer estimated an overnight loss of £2000 and another nearby, £1000. The early potato industry in western Britain is an example of a specialised intensive form of agricultural production which is sensitive to the frost hazard, which even if it does not kill the plant, can cause checks in the growth that affect the timing and scale of yields and ultimately profits. Orchard crops seem to be at greatest risk from spring frosts in central Kent, north-east Hampshire and in the Avon valley from Pershore to Stratford-on-Avon, while coastal market gardening areas such as the Sussex coast are almost always frost free. At East Malling Research Station in Kent, frosts have caused severe loss of yield in about 1 year in 6, although effects on fruit quality are more frequent.

Information on snowfall and snow cover is provided by a special network of about 190 stations (see Fig. 3.4). The Glaciological Society set up the original network of Snow Survey stations in 1937. Before its recent demise, annual reports appeared in *British rainfall*, but now the snow statistics are published annually by the Meteorological Office as a Snow Survey Report and include details of the number of days of snow falling and snow lying and the maximum depths attained. There has been no systematic recording and reporting of the mechanical and physical properties of fallen snow or of its thermal properties. The incidence of snowfall, like that of severe winters and low temperatures, varies considerably so that maps such as Figure 3.5 showing the average number of days with snow lying at 09.00 hours GMT must be used with caution, since averages for another 30-year period may be quite different. In general though, as Jackson (1977b) has pointed out the use of figures from the most recent period is more realistic for planning purposes than those for the very 'un-snowy' period of 1901–40. The very important role played by altitude in determining the frequency with which snow lies is obvious from Figure 3.5. In a recent paper (Jackson 1978) use has been made of the median rather than the mean to express frequency of snow lying. This gets around the problem that the mean is affected appreciably by abnormally high or low values, for example a very severe winter, in a 30-year period. Values of the number of days with snow lying in a median winter reduced to sea level are shown in Figure 3.6 and show a fairly simple pattern over Great Britain with a gradient from southwest to northeast.

Since it is heavy falling snow which most frequently causes transport disruption, estimates such as that in Figure 3.7 are of particular interest. Jackson calculates that at a typical Midland location, such as Birmingham airport (Elmdon), snowfall accumulation will be of the order of 8·5 cm in one hour and 20·4 cm in 24 hours, with a return period of 10 years. On about 25% of occasions when moderate or heavy snow is falling the temperature and wind speed conditions will be suitable for drifting to take place. In Scotland, even when snow is lying in western coastal areas it is usually less than 2 cm deep, but in the east and north much greater depths are probable. At Wick in Caithness, 10·1% of the reports of snow lying had depths greater than 16 cm and at Balmoral the percentage was 19·1%. The effect of surface obstacles on wind movement frequently results in very varied depths and distribution patterns of snowfall. Thus it can happen that snow is swept off open fields, but fills nearby sunken lanes which act as receptacles and may be filled to the tops of their hedgerows. It should also be noted that in Britain snow lying is one of the most variable climatological elements, and averages have to be computed from widely different values in different years. In Figure 3.8 the depth of level snow

Figure 3.6 Number of days with snow lying in a median winter reduced to sea level. Calculated from 1941–70 means (after Jackson 1978).

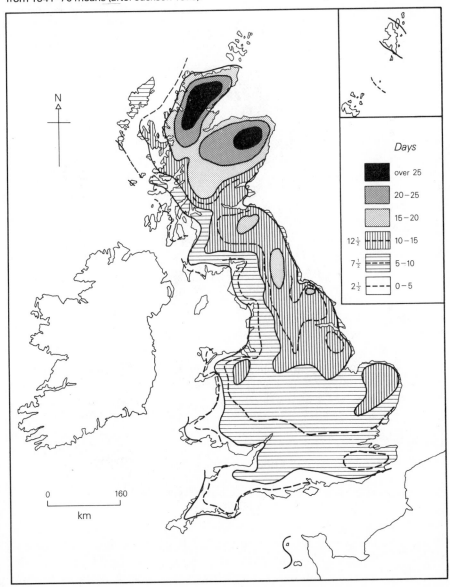

reached or exceeded in 10 winters per century is shown and this data has been taken into account in constructing Table 3.2. In our worst storms depths of 30–60 cm may accumulate over a wide area. In virtually every part of the country snow has been over 40 cm deep at some time in the last 100 years, except near some western coasts. Reynolds (1954) calculated that on Merseyside a depth of 60 cm of snow might only be expected once in 1000 years. In the 1962–3

Figure 3.7   Estimated mean annual number of hours of moderate or heavy snow (after Jackson 1977).

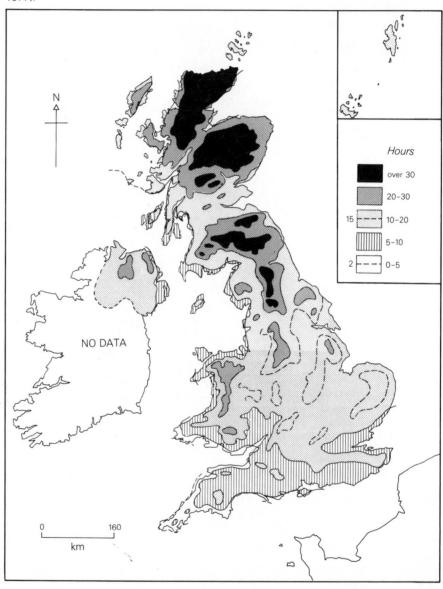

Figure 3.8 Depth of level snow reached or exceeded in 10 winters per century.

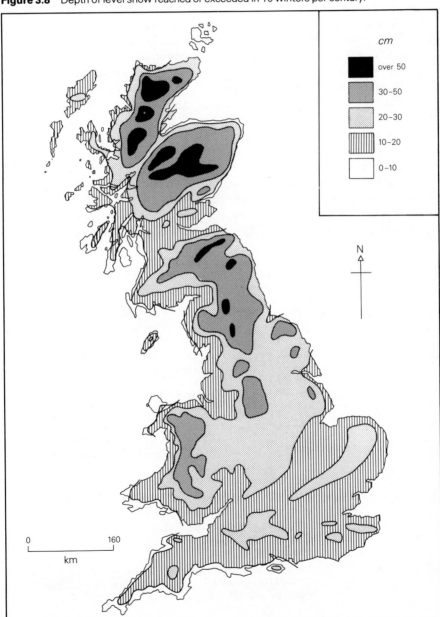

winter, depths of 165 cm and 75 cm were reported from Tredegar in South Wales and Bellingham in Northumberland respectively, while about 150 cm are stated to have fallen in the Isle of Wight and Hampshire in January 1881. Recently, radar measurements of areal snow depths have been attempted (Collier & Larke 1978).

The large-scale weather patterns leading to substantial falls of snow have been discussed by Lowndes (1971). Most of the 562 substantial snowfalls (water equivalent greater than 7 mm in 24 hours) in the years 1954–69 were associated with either a warm front or warm occlusion approaching from between south and west, or a polar low or trough in a northerly airstream.

Many of the most severe blizzards experienced over southern England in the past 100 years have been associated with a depression moving slowly up the English Channel giving very strong easterly or north-easterly winds. Of the total number of occasions with substantial snowfall, only 57% resulted in a complete snow cover which persisted for at least 24 hours, and on only 17% of occasions did the snow persist for 5 days or more.

A fortunately fairly rare winter hazard in the British Isles is glazed frost, which consists of a coat of ice formed by rain or drizzle falling on to a surface whose temperature is below freezing point. Glazed frost on roads is popularly known as black ice. Localised occurrences sometimes develop after a long cold spell as warmer air advances over still-frozen ground, but very occasionally

Table 3.2   A hierarchy of disruption due to snow and ice in the British Isles.

	Effects	Comments
1st order – paralysing	Blocked roads, paralysis of communications, isolated rural settlements, power failures, major absenteeism in schools and at places of work. Rescue work undertaken by air, major livestock losses on hill farms.	25–30 cm of level undrifted snow. Return period in southern England about 15–20 years.
2nd order – crippling	Communications difficult with only essential journeys by road advised by police. Cancellation of most outdoor sporting events. Closure of rural schools.	Accompanies 10–20 cm of level snow in lowland England. Return period of 5–10 years in the south of England.
3rd order – inconvenience	Traffic movement impaired with increase in accidents attributable to snow and ice conditions. Sporting events affected.	Occurs on average every other year in southern districts.
4th order – nuisance	Traffic movement slowed, minimal press coverage. Gritting lorries rather than snowploughs required.	Can be expected to occur every winter, except in extreme SW

persistent and widespread glazed frost can occur, if the advancing milder air is held up for several days. An occurrence in late January 1940 has been described by Brooks and Douglas (1956) and was thought to be due to an exceptional combination of factors unlikely to recur over a long period. Great damage was caused to telegraph poles and wires and to wildlife. Page (1969) described an occurrence in Yorkshire in March 1969, which totally stopped commercial televison services in the area due to the destruction of the transmitting mast at Emley Moor as well as severely disrupting electricity and telephone services.

Costs and effects of the hazard

Although a few descriptive accounts have been written of the economic impact of the snow and frost hazard in the British Isles (e.g. Burroughs 1978), there are no comparable methodological studies to those undertaken in the USA by Rooney (1967). Some of the techniques used to appraise disruption in these studies are applicable in the context of the British Isles, and in Table 3.2 a hierarchy of disruption is presented based on a study of past events (see Jackson 1977a), and using Rooney's ordering scheme. The table is designed to provide only general guidance, since the amount of disruption caused by a single fall of snow will depend on many factors including whether the snow is wet and sticky, how much wind and hence drifting accompanies the fall, and the state of preparedness of snow-clearing teams. Probably the most important factor determining the human response to snowfall is the frequency with which heavy falls can be expected in a given community. This can be illustrated by constructing a classification of disruption and using sources such as local newspaper reports to compare the frequency of disruption in different communities. A simple classification was used:

Class 1   Communications within the town and between the town and its surroundings disrupted or curtailed.
Class 2   Communications within the town only disrupted.
Class 3   No transport disruption, but mention made of snowfall.

Data for the 10 winters 1959–60 to 1968–9 were obtained for the similar-sized towns of Buxton, Derbyshire (height 335 m) and Northwich, Cheshire (height 15 m) and is shown in Table 3.3.

Table 3.3   Frequency of disruption from snow occurring in Buxton and Northwich.

	Buxton	Northwich
Class 1	19	3
Class 2	7	5
Class 3	19	12
Total	45	20

Figure 3.9   Disruption to communications in the countryside as snow is blown from fields to fill the lanes which act as natural receptacles.

Figure 3.10   Urban snow disrupts social and economic life but provides additional temporary employment for casual workers. City streets may require not only clearing but also snow hauling to open spaces may be necessary since the physical space to dump cleared snow is often not available.

In Buxton most Class 1 disruptions occurred when the total depth of snow lying was greater than 20 cm but in Northwich a fall of 10 cm could cause this scale of disruption. It was found that in Buxton urban dwellers were highly aware of the damages and delays which are a normal part of their winter life, while at Northwich respondents to a questionnaire survey revealed they were unconcerned about the snow hazard, and a high degree of concern was exhibited about other weather elements such as fog. From surveys of this type it can be concluded that experience plays a large part in determining the amount of dislocation that snow causes. Where experience of heavy snow is limited the amount of disruption is likely to be greater (see Figs. 3.9 and 3.10).

It is appropriate to include in this account Rooney's (1967) useful conceptual framework of the urban snow hazard (Fig. 3.11) which effectively displays some of the relationships that exist between 'urban man' and his snow environment, and in particular emphasises that the kind of adjustments made to counteract the hazard are based in part on the individual's choice (e.g. does he buy snow chains for his car), and in part on collective action. Paralysing disruption will reduce communities to a state of suspended animation, and occurs following major blizzards. Although such events may represent a component of a severe

Figure 3.11 Conceptual framework of the urban snow hazard (after Rooney 1967).

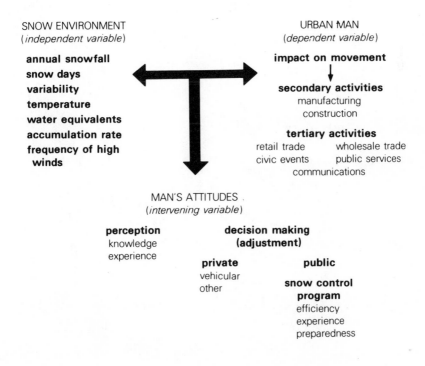

THE URBAN SNOW HAZARD

A CONCEPTUAL FRAMEWORK

winter, they can accompany short cold spells in winters with normal temperatures (as in southern England and South Wales in February 1978).

High-altitude settlements in the North take such precautions as laying in stocks of tinned foods in the autumn as a matter of course, while in the normally mild south-west of England the occasional heavy snowfall can be far more disruptive and economically damaging. The threshold of crippling snowfall varies greatly from area to area and, as Burton, Kates and White (1978) point out, the common physical units of measurement may be unsuited for assessment of social impact.

The severity of the impact of extremely cold winters can best be judged by recalling the experiences of 1947 and 1962–3. Britain was struggling to recover from the shortages and deprivations of wartime in 1947, and fuel supplies in particular were less than adequate when the severe weather struck. Electricity restrictions became necessary in early February with domestic supplies cut off for up to 5 hours a day. The consequences of these restrictions to industry was that workers had to be temporarily laid-off with the result that unemployment reached 2 million for a short time. The index of production fell by 25%, although the effect was short-lived, with output returning to normal by April. The effects of the winter on agriculture were catastrophic as can be seen in Figure 3.12, with the country's sheep flock being reduced by about 4 million (about 20% of the total) and with mortality rates reaching 80–90% in the hardest-hit farming regions.

The impact of the prolonged 1962–3 severe winter was less dramatic, since the strength of the economy at the time was healthier and energy supplies were more plentiful. Nevertheless economic activity dropped by about 7%, un-

Figure 3.12   The effect of the 1947 winter on agricultural production (after Burroughs 1978).

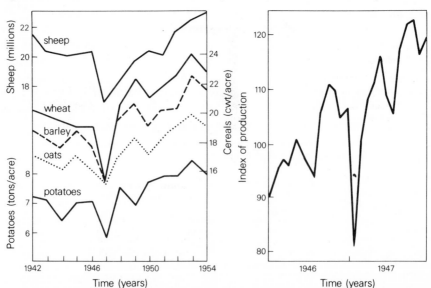

employment increased and, with the cessation of outdoor building and construction work, 160 000 workers were laid off, entailing pay losses of some £30 millions. Electricity and gas consumption was nearly 20% above that in a normal winter and power disconnections proved necessary, in part due to industrial strike action during the cold weather. At 1979 values the insurance companies paid out in the region of £70 millions, mostly as claims for damage to carpets, walls and furniture caused by water leaking from burst pipes. At least 49 people were killed by the direct effects of the severe weather and at one time more than 150 000 km of road were blocked, and as in 1947 the South West was the district most badly hit.

Road transport is particularly vulnerable to both frost and snow and the disruptive effects of wintry weather conditions has become something of a national joke. Recent experience shows that a shallow snow cover of 2 cm or less in thickness may be sufficient to hinder or even halt traffic, since on our crowded roads a slight disturbance of traffic flow can quickly grow to block the flow. The cost of extra journey times includes work losses, late delivery of goods, losses of consumer sales and receipt losses on public transport. Accidents caused by slippery roads during snow and icy conditions inevitably increase. On average casualties were increased by 25% on snowy days though the casualty rate per unit of traffic was nearly doubled (OECD 1976). In the case of major new roads in high-altitude environments, for example the M62 across the Pennines, winter maintenance requirements can be minimised by planning at the highway design stage. Cuttings and embankments can affect snow drifting and accumulation and need to be carefully planned. Snowdrifts are formed by the intrusion into the snow-laden wind stream of obstacles which cause the formation of wind eddies, with consequent deposition of snow. By suiting the highway to its surroundings no opportunity is provided for the snow to settle on the carriageway, e.g. the use of parapets to guide the wind and the snow over the road. In financial terms it has been estimated that the average increase in costs of accidents due to snow and ice is in the order of £3 millions annually. The Highways Act 1959 (Section 129) made county and local highway authorities responsible for keeping their roads free from ice and snow. The spreading of rock salt (salting) has become the preferred method of meeting this statute in many places since it is capable of melting ice at temperatures as low as −21°C and some 2 million tons are used annually at a cost in excess of £7 millions. Unfortunately rock salt increases vehicle corrosion and causes environmental damage, and a study group – The Atmosphere–Road Surface Interaction Study Group at University College, London – is now examining its use (Thornes, Wood & Blackmore 1977). Since it is desirable to keep the use of salt on roads to a minimum it is essential to restrict its use to occasions when it is really necessary and this depends on meteorological and road surface conditions. It has been estimated that in Britain we are spreading at least twice as much rock salt on our roads than is actually needed to prevent the accumulation of ice and snow. Research is currently being carried out in an attempt to improve the accuracy of the Road Danger Warnings issued by local meteorological offices to highway authorities leading to a reduction in 'oversalting'. The London Weather Centre issues Road Danger Warnings for South East England at 15.00 hours for the following evening and night, and decisions are then made as to whether the 60 maintenance engineers in the region need to be contacted so that gritting crews can be put on to the roads. A typical road danger warning is of the form 'Road surface temperatures are expected to fall below freezing point after midnight, but most roads are expected to remain dry'.

Figure 3.13   Reasons prompting local authorities to treat road surfaces.

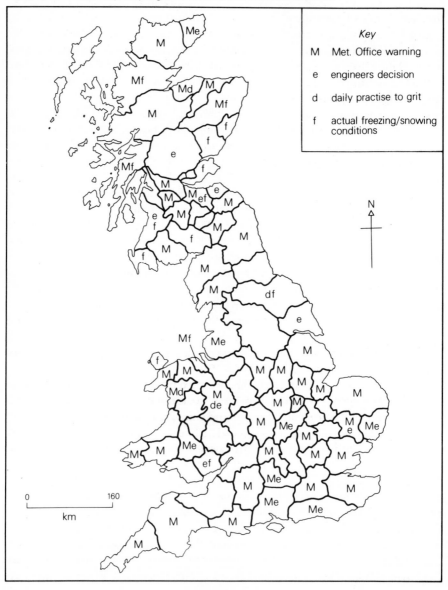

Not all local authorities receive an official meteorological warning. Figure 3.13 shows that some authorities actually wait for freezing conditions to occur before taking any action while others salt their roads regularly, if the maintenance engineer is wary of the conditions. It is probable that these authorities consider that the available forecasts are not local enough for their needs. It is the maintenance engineer who has to face angry members of the public who may have skidded and crashed on their way to work on an icy road. There is thus a tendency to play safe and salt the roads whenever ice is a faint possibility. Snow falling overnight is likely to cause most trouble on the roads because a layer can build up without disturbance by traffic. Most highway authorities aim to ensure that roads are in such a condition that essential traffic can move with reasonable speed and safety. The success of a winter maintenance operation depends on rapid mobilisation before the onset of adverse conditions. Where preventative measures are only irregularly in demand, for example on low ground in South West England, they tend to be less highly organised and slower to be put into effect than in places which have more frequent frost and snow. Evidence that local authority plans for dealing with snow emergencies remain imperfect was demonstrated following blizzards in the first few days of 1979. Public expenditure cuts and disputes over standby payments for manual staff undoubtedly contributed to the inadequate clearing of some major roads on this occasion. During the 1978–9 winter the National Bus Company estimated it had incurred costs of £15 millions in repairs to their vehicles and in lost revenue.

On roads where the occurrence of ice, frost and snow makes motoring especially dangerous over short critical lengths, e.g. on bridge decks or ramps leading to underpasses or flyovers, road heaters may be installed. Because of their large capital and operating costs such devices are only used at very critical locations in urban areas, for example on the Chiswick Viaduct of the M4, and on the Tinsley Viaduct in Yorkshire. Lath and wire type snow fences are used alongside exposed roads in Scotland and in some English counties such as Oxfordshire. When carefully planned, vegetation can form an effective and cheap protection against snow drifting, while at the same time helping to beautify the landscape.

The effects of snow and ice can be mitigated by forecasts allowing preventative measures to be taken. In rural areas stock can be housed, or moved from exposed upland areas, while in towns and cities gritting and salting of roads can be started before the onset of snowfall. Snow, ice and frost warnings are included when appropriate in weather bulletins broadcast on radio and television and facilities exist for 'weather flashes' to be inserted between programmes if necessary to warn of the expected onset of specified weather in a stated locality. In addition, weather information is frequently included in programmes about road and traffic conditions and special forecasts can be obtained by industries or individual firms with weather-sensitive activities. On some occasions however, the reactions of the general public can be unpredictable and can increase the chaos that snow and ice so frequently bring. Stringer (1970) has documented some examples of the reactions of Birmingham commuters to snow during the

1967–8 winter. Heavy snowfall early on 9 January 1968 suspended railway operations in the area because British Rail were relying on an incorrect national forecast which predicted a thaw. Birmingham City Corporation, however, followed an accurate locally available forecast and cleared the roads ready for the morning rush hour. Unfortunately, most commuters, on waking to find snow, elected to leave their cars at home and attempted to travel by the suspended rail services. Such a case study emphasises the point that the impact of weather hazards depends to a large extent on the accuracy and communication of national and local weather forecasts. In addition, organisations such as the Automobile Association are able to provide regular road condition reports which are made available for members telephoning a local AA office.

Drivers who become stranded in snowdrifts can suffer seriously from exposure, particularly if they attempt to abandon their vehicles to seek shelter. One suggestion made after the severe blizzards in north-east Scotland in January 1978 was that upland roads might be fitted with gates on the approach to exposed areas notorious for drifting snow, which could then be closed by police when snow was forecast. The Drumochter Pass on the Perth–Inverness road has had gates fitted at its north end, but experience in February 1979 suggested that blizzards can occur so quickly that there is no opportunity for local authorities to close them with the result that hotels and church halls can become crammed with stranded motorists using them as relief shelters. Damage to road surfaces can easily result from prolonged periods of severe weather when frost penetrates into road foundations. Saving on surface dressing can be false economy if it results in damage to the roads' foundations necessitating expensive reconstruction work.

During prolonged cold spells the ground may freeze to depths of up to 20 m, and in 1962–3 on well drained sand and gravel, frost was noted at 0·6 m. Under such conditions pavements and road surfaces can be cracked and uplifted by frost heave. Severe frosts in winter allow unlagged pipes to freeze and the resulting damage to furnishings following a thaw can result in expensive damage for householders. The recent spread of double glazing, cavity wall filling and higher standard of insulation on recently built houses can be regarded as an adjustment process to combat the effect of cold weather accelerated by the rising cost of fossil fuels in recent years.

Detailed accounts have appeared of the rail transport problems that can follow snow and ice conditions (Canovan 1971, Parrey 1970). Because of the heavy demands made by commuters early in the morning there is a need, particularly on British Rail Southern Region, to anticipate bad weather. Anti-icing procedures include running special trains through the night to coat conductor rails with antifreeze, and activating heated points, which have been installed in increasing numbers at busy junctions in recent years. Even with the use of snow-ploughs, trains can be trapped and buried in our worst blizzards, especially in Scotland. In January 1978, two trains and a relief engine snowplough were trapped near Wick in Caithness and passengers had to be rescued by helicopter. Snow frequently causes curtailment of aircraft movements, in part because visibility is usually very poor when snow is falling, and also because snow and ice on runways has to be cleared before they can be used. Aircraft have been used since at least 1940 to rescue people trapped in blizzards and to drop supplies. One of the earliest of the large-scale operations was mounted in January 1955 in north and east Scotland and became known as 'Operation Snowdrop'. Helicopters have now replaced fixed-wing aircraft as the most suitable type of transport for these operations. On 30 January 1978, 350 people were rescued by air after the northeast Scotland blizzards, in what was described as the biggest airborne rescue operation ever to be mounted in Europe (Symons & Perry 1979).

Wintry weather hazards affect agriculture in a variety of ways. After heavy snowfall it may be impossible to get fodder to animals except by air. Airlifting animal feed by helicopter is normally speedily arranged after a paralysing blizzard, but as in the West Country snowstorms in February 1978, uncertainty may arise over who would pay the costs involved. Because delay can be crucial, disputes of this kind emphasise the need for pre-planning before emergency situations arise. Commercial dairy farming is dependent on regular, efficient transport of milk from the farms, and when this becomes impossible, thousands of gallons of milk may have to be poured away leading to considerable financial loss. Wet snow may bring down overhead power lines depriving rural areas of electricity supplies for periods and presenting a further problem to the farmer needing to operate electric milking machines. Sheep can survive for some time if covered by snow because their own coats insulate them against loss of body heat, but persistent deep snow in upland areas can lead to heavy stock losses. In 1978 the Scottish Office estimated that about 2000 sheep were lost in Shetland and between 8–10 000 in the Highland region in the blizzards. On many farms livestock numbers have been greatly increased in recent years to maximise profitability on the assumption that feeding stuffs can readily be brought in, and the balance between the fodder resources of the farm and the stock carried is no longer the closely calculated matter that was formerly regarded as an essential part of farming.

For the sheep farmer the spring lambing period represents his hardest time, and heavy snowfall at this time can lead to ewes becoming weak and a high incidence of lambs born dead. Even though compensation may be made available to the farmer after such stock losses, he may need to borrow money before this is received, and thus face heavy interest charges.

The severity of impact of frost depends not only on the temperature but also

Table 3.4 Standard frost classification used in the British Isles.

Description of frost	Windspeed < 10 knots	Windspeed > 10 knots
slight	0·0° to −3·5°C	0·0° to −0·4°C
moderate	−3·6° to −6·4°C	−0·5° to −2·4°C
severe	−6·5° to −11·5°C	−2·5° to −5·5°C
very severe	below −11·6°C	below −5·6°C

on the windspeed. The standard frost classification shown in Table 3.4 shows that a temperature only just below freezing can produce a penetrating frost when wind speeds are high.

Damage to the flowers of commercial fruit-bearing plants by frost is probably the commonest frost effect of economic significance. Various preventative measures are available to the farmer and horticulturalist to minimise the effects of spring frosts. A reliable assessment of the risk allows the farmer to plan his use of the land, and to avoid growing sensitive crops in the most frost-prone areas. Commercial orchards are frequently planted on sloping ground where damage by frost is less likely than in valley bottom situations. On the assumption that slopes of at least 2 degrees are necessary to support cold-air katabatic drainage it is possible, using large scale contour maps, to produce maps similar to Figure 3.14 indicating areas from which cold air flows (donor areas) and areas into which it flows (reception areas). Once the farmer knows the vulnerability of his crop and the gross return expected per acre he is in a position to estimate probable losses due to the frost hazard or assess the cost–benefit situation of providing equipment to reduce the hazard. As rising costs have narrowed the margins for profitable fruit production so studies of climate, and especially of frost incidence have become increasingly relevant. Meteorologists are able to forecast spring frosts fairly accurately, and the agriculturalist may decide to limit the risk by a variety of special actions, including smoke generation, the use of oil-burning heaters and overhead sprinkling. The latter technique involves the continuous application of a fine water spray to the surface of the crop, the temperature of which then does not fall below freezing point. Some figures published by Bush (1945) emphasise why the horticulturalist will go to considerable lengths to minimise frost damage. Apple yields in relatively frost-prone Britain vary by as much as 298% between lowest and highest yearly values, whereas in less frosty countries the variation is much lower, e.g. Australia 17%. Agricultural enterprises specialising in the production of out-of-season or early crops may be affected by prolonged spells of wintry weather. In January 1979 £500 000 worth of damage to Jersey's cauliflower crop was reported. Protracted cold weather leads to heavy expenditure on fuel for heating glasshouses and growers can sustain unexpectedly heavy costs which may not be fully recouped when crops are harvested. Early flower production in areas like the Isles of Scilly is geared to supplying the market at such times of peak demand as 'Mother's Day' and a late spring may retard bulb growth so that flowers are not available in quantity at the required time. The consequences of a given frost level can vary according to the type of weather that has preceded the frost. The same spring frost level will be more damaging to fruit trees if it follows mild weather that has accelerated growth, than if it follows a period of low temperature which seems to harden the buds.

Perhaps the most serious and tragic effect of cold weather is its toll of human life, particularly of the elderly. More than 2 million old people live in temperatures which would lead to prosecution if they occurred in factories or offices. The charitable organisation 'Help the Aged' believes that in a bad winter, there

Figure 3.14 Areas of katabatic drainage in Somerset and crop suitability regions.

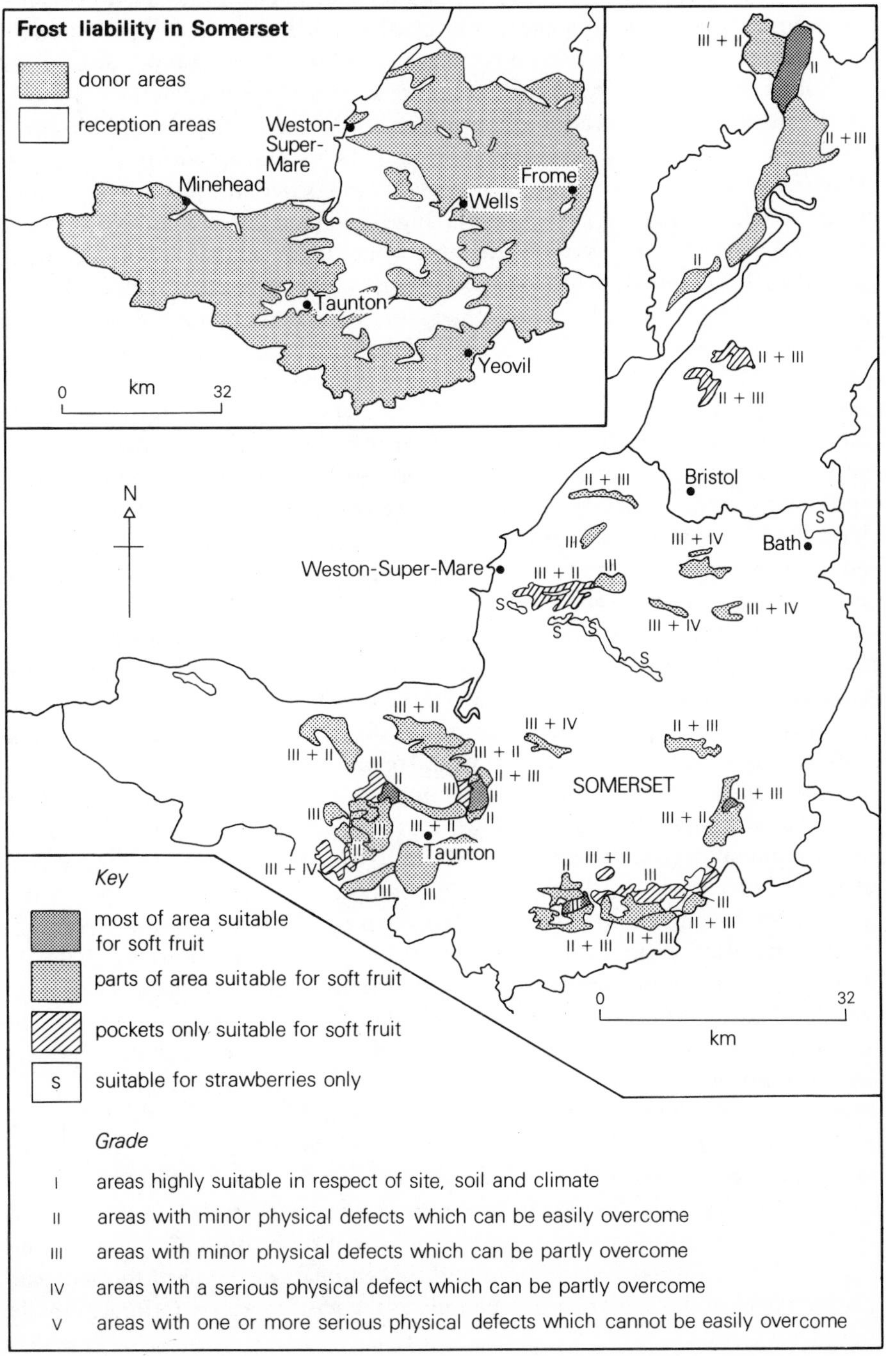

Frost liability in Somerset

- donor areas
- reception areas

Weston-Super-Mare
Minehead
Frome
Wells
Taunton
Yeovil

0   km   32

III + II
II
II + III
II
II + III
II + III

N

II + III   Bristol

III   III + IV   Bath
Weston-Super-Mare   III + II   III   S
S   III + IV
III + IV

III + II
III + II   III + IV   II + III
III + II
III   II   SOMERSET   II + III
III   III + II   II + III   III + II
III
III + II   II
III + IV   Taunton
III   III + II   III
III   III   II + III
II + III   II + III
I + III

Key

- most of area suitable for soft fruit
- parts of area suitable for soft fruit
- pockets only suitable for soft fruit
- S | suitable for strawberries only

0   32
km

Grade

I   areas highly suitable in respect of site, soil and climate
II   areas with minor physical defects which can be easily overcome
III areas with minor physical defects which can be partly overcome
IV   areas with a serious physical defect which can be partly overcome
V   areas with one or more serious physical defects which cannot be easily overcome

are as many as 80 000 deaths from the effects of the cold. Although thousands die every year from cold-associated diseases, the trigger factor hypothermia, or loss of body temperature, rarely appears on a death certificate. However, it is recognised that it is frequently the cold which has started a heart attack, pneumonia or bronchitis. At a conservative estimate 700 000 pensioners risk hypothermia each winter. A detailed national survey is needed of the old at risk, with more generous heating allowances, insulation schemes and widespread publicity if these figures are to be reduced. Personal snow control, for example shovelling paths or driveways clear of snow, can prove an effective trigger for a heart attack, particularly of people with high blood pressure not used to vigorous physical activities. The West Midlands coroner reported that in one evening in January 1977 five men in his area died because of the physical rigours of clearing snow. The men, aged between 52 and 76, went out to clear the snow from outside their houses and all collapsed and died of coronary heart disease within minutes. All had been well in the morning and the coroner blamed the biting cold wind rather than the actual air temperature and concluded that snow clearance should be left to teenagers and healthy adults who are used to strenuous physical activity. In fact householders who clear snow from pavements in front of their houses can face legal trouble. Legal opinion regards snow as a natural hazard and if a pedestrian slips on untouched snow he can take no action. Once an effort is made to clear the snow a claim for liability can be made. The old and infirm are the most likely to suffer from broken bones following falls if they venture out while snow and ice are still lying. The aftermath of a long freezing spell can bring tragedy particularly to children using rivers and ponds for skating, who may face drowning as the ice breaks up. Severe winter weather, particularly if it is prolonged can seriously affect wild animal communities. The 1962–3 winter was particularly damaging to some species of wild birds, including for example the Dartford Warbler, and it took many years for the numbers to rise again. Increasing numbers of people visit the uplands and mountains of Britain in winter to walk and climb. Mountain rescue teams have been called out frequently to tourists suffering from hypothermia and exposure resulting from inadequate or unsuitable clothing. Rain-soaked clothing can quickly reduce body temperatures to dangerously low values, and as Smithson and Baldwin (1979) have noted, visitors frequently arrive in the artificial warmth of a car, and are unprepared for outside climatic conditions. One way of assessing the cooling power of the atmosphere is the windchill index, which expresses the cooling power of the wind for various combinations of temperature and windspeed. Physiological experiments with an index of windchill for clothed persons developed by Steadman (1971) have shown that for values greater than 400 cal m^{-2} s^{-1} exposed flesh will freeze. It seems that values above this figure occur comparatively frequently in the British uplands, and during very cold spells on lower ground also. Even during the summer months, wind cooling can produce unpleasant conditions and this emphasises the need for adequate protective clothing at all times, especially as the weather can deteriorate rapidly in upland areas.

At high altitudes not only cold but also blizzards and whiteout conditions occur over a comparatively long season. In 1971 a severe blizzard as early in the season as 21 November led to the deaths of a teacher and five children in the Cairngorms. Despite being equipped with emergency food rations and spare clothes, exposure in atrocious conditions, which had not been foreseen by the party, proved fatal. Higher standards of mountain leadership certificates can help to avert such tragedies but there is very little to stop the lone climber and walker from venturing on to the British uplands where, even if he is experienced, the combination of wind, cold, slippery icy surfaces, occasional avalanches and snow cornices can often prove disastrous. Avalanches have been recorded in places other than the high mountains of Scotland; on 28 January 1979 a climber was swept to his death in the western Pennines near Oldham. One of the few disastrous avalanches recorded in lowland England occurred on 27 December 1836 at Lewes, Sussex. Eight people were killed and several houses were demolished when a cornice of snow collapsed. A public house named the 'Snow Drop' has been built at the point where the disaster happened. Even in high summer, exposure can result in areas like the Cairngorms for walkers, particularly if they lose their way, and it is necessary from time to time to make use of helicopters to rescue and transport to hospital afflicted persons.

Snow and frost can disrupt sporting fixtures, such as football matches and race meetings, causing financial losses, not only to particular participants and organisers but also to the whole gambling industry. The vulnerability of horse racing is shown by the fact that in 1976, a year without major long cold spells, over 30 race meetings had to be abandoned.

Conclusions

As a technically advanced urban society we have at our disposal the organisational and technological abilities to deal successfully with the range of winter weather hazards described in this chapter. However, because wintry weather conditions seldom last long, and severe winters occur with a frequency of little more than one a decade, our degree of preparedness for meeting this hazard is such that annoyance and disruption occur at the onset of frost, snow and ice, movement is effectively curtailed while the old and sick are often put at risk. Although after a severe winter there is often a clamour for additional public expenditure on such items as snowploughs, memories tend to be short and both as individuals and communities we remain normally unprepared for the next visitation. It is not only the magnitude of the snow event, but also the work patterns, modes of transportation and degree of urbanisation that have contributed heavily to snow's disruptive effects on society. Although some snowfall is the normal expectation every winter over the moors, hills and higher ground of the North and West of the British Isles, elsewhere heavy snowfall is likely to be sufficiently rare to be seen merely as a possibility rather than a contingency that enters into most people's plans for their everyday lives. Manley, writing in

1952, said 'it remains to be seen whether in 1980 we shall continue to describe winter extremes as dangerously rare'. Time has shown that such a phrase remains appropriate considering the inadequacy of the provisions that we make.

Bibliography

Brooks, C. E. P. and C. K. M. Douglas 1956. *Glazed frost of January 1940*. Geophys. Mem., no. 98. Bracknell, England: Met. Office.

Burroughs, W. 1978. Cold winters and the economy. *New Scientist* **75**, 326–8.

Bush, R. 1945. *Frost and the fruit grower*. London: Cassell and Co.

Canovan, R. A. 1971. Wintry prospects for British Rail. *Weather* **26**, 472–91.

Collier, C. G. and P. R. Larke 1978. A case study of the measurement of snowfall by radar – an assessment of accuracy. *Q. J. R. Meteorol. Soc.* **104**, 444–7.

Folland, C. K. 1975. A relationship between cool summers in Central England and the temperature of the following winter for summers occurring in an even year. *Weather* **30**, 348–58.

Hay, J. S. and C. P. Young 1972. Weather forecasting for the prevention of icy roads in the UK. In *Weather forecasting for agriculture and industry*, J. S. Taylor (ed.), 155–65. Newton Abbot: David and Charles.

Hopkins, J. S. and K. W. Whyte 1975. Extreme temperatures over the UK for design purposes. *Meteorol. Mag.* **104**, 94–102.

Hornigold, P. C. 1970. *The winter maintenance of roads with particular reference to the snow problem*. Univ. of Leeds PhD thesis (unpublished).

Hunt, K. E. 1967. *The economics of frost*. Aberystwyth Mem., no. 10. Aberystwyth: Univ. Coll. of Wales.

Jackson, M. C. 1977a. A classification of the snowiness of 100 winters – a tribute to the late L. C. W. Bonacina. *Weather* **32**, 91–7.

Jackson, M. C. 1977b. The occurrence of falling snow over the UK. *Meteorol. Mag.* **106**, 26–38.

Jackson, M. C. 1978. Snow cover in Great Britain. *Weather* **33**, 298–308.

Lowndes, C. A. S. 1971. Substantial snowfalls over the UK 1954–69. *Meteorol. Mag.* **100**, 193–207.

Lyness, F. K. and H. M. Badger 1970. A measure of winter severity. *Appl. Stat.* **19**, 119–34.

Manley, G. 1952. *Climate and the British scene*. New Naturalist Series. London: Collins.

Namias, J. 1963. Large scale air–sea interactions over the N. Pacific from summer 1962 through the subsequent winter. *J. Geophys. Res.* **68**, 617–8.

OECD 1976. *Adverse weather, reduced visibility and road safety*. Paris: OECD.

Page, J. K. 1969. Heavy glaze in Yorkshire – March 1969. *Weather* **24**, 486–95.

Parrey, C. E. 1970. A railway problem during the heavy snowfall of March 1970. *Meteorol. Mag.* **99**, 299–304.

Reynolds, G. 1954. Snowfall probabilities on Merseyside. *Q. J. R. Meteorol. Soc.* **80**, 444–7.

Rooney, J. F. 1967. The urban snow hazard in the US – an appraisal of disruption. *Geogl Rev.* **57**, 538–59.

Shellard, H. C. 1968. The winter of 1962–3 in the UK – a climatological survey. *Meteorol. Mag.* **97**, 129–41.

Smithson, P. A. and H. Baldwin 1979. Windchill in upland areas. *Weather* **34**, 294–306.

Steadman, R. G. 1971. Indices of windchill of clothed persons. *J. Appl. Meteorol.* **10**, 674–83.

Stringer, E. T. 1970. The use of cost–benefit studies in the interpretation of probability forecasts for agriculture and industry. In *Weather economics,* J. A. Taylor (ed.), 83–92. Oxford: Pergamon.

Symons, L. and A. H. Perry 1979. The blizzards of early 1978, and the use of helicopters to alleviate the resulting economic and social disruption. *Disaster* **3**, 8–12.

Taylor, J. A. 1967. *Frost: its physical, biological and economic significance.* Aberystwyth Mem., no. 10. Aberystwyth: Univ. Coll. of Wales.

Thornes, J., L. Wood and R. Blackmore 1977. To salt or not to salt. *New Scientist* **75**, 326–8.

4 The flood hazard

'The rain descended and the floods came'

Matthew 7:25

The nature of the hazard

Flooding is among the commonest environmental hazard experienced in the British Isles despite concerted efforts by planners and civil engineers to reduce the danger and damage caused. It is also probably the best documented and described hazard. In addition to numerous research papers there are at least three books – *Flooding and the flood hazard in the UK* (Newson 1975); *Floods* (Ward 1978); and *Human adjustment to the flood hazard* (Smith & Tobin 1979) – that consider the hazard and that the interested reader is recommended to consult. Hydrologists define river floods in terms of frequency, thus the annual flood would be the largest flow during a year, or in terms of the geometry of the river channel. Since we are concerned only with floods which, because of their intensity or destructive force cause damage, a more general definition of flooding seems appropriate. Hewitt and Burton (1971) have suggested – 'harmful inundation of property and land utilised by man'; while Ward suggests – 'a flood is a body of water which rises to overflow land which is not normally submerged'.

The flood hazard is the joint product of physical and human factors, and flooding is as much an economic problem as a hydrological one. In the case of rivers, the low-lying floodplain bordering the river is susceptible to inundation, but the floodplain exhibits natural site factors which in many instances have made it an attractive settlement site. By responding to these factors and attempting a land-use which is not in harmony with the hydrological cycle, Man is subject to the flood hazard, although he frequently seeks to reduce the flood threat by investing in preventative measures. In a study of the flood hazard we need to consider meteorological factors, such as the incidence of heavy rainfall,

Table 4.1 Examples of flood damage and benefits.

Tangible		Intangible	Benefits
Direct	Indirect		
property damage	loss of trading profit	anxiety	added fertility of agricultural land from silt
drowning of humans, animals and crops	traffic disruption	inconvenience	groundwater resources recharged

hydrological conditions such as catchment characteristics and human–hazard producing factors.

It is customary to distinguish between tangible and intangible flood damage based on whether or not monetary values can be assigned to the consequences of flooding, and in Table 4.1 examples of each are given, together with examples of benefits derived from flooding. Loss of life, the distress caused by property damage and the suffering that results from the dislocation of the economic life of communities are well known concomitants of a major flood. In 1978 Porter estimated mean annual flood losses in England and Wales to be about £10 millions with up to £6 millions spent on flood alleviation in any one year. In any flood the majority of the damage is frequently borne by a handful of properties and large savings can be achieved particularly by protecting business premises. Smith and Tobin (1979) found that in the 1968 floods in the Cumbrian Eden, just three businesses in Carlisle and one in Appleby suffered one-third of the total losses, although one-tenth of the land area of the city of Carlisle was affected by flooding.

A review of floods

Inland flooding. The meteorological conditions leading to inland flooding involve intense precipitation, prolonged precipitation or snowmelt, either singly or acting in combination. Studies of actual falls of heavy rain can most easily be undertaken for the 'rainfall day' (09.00–09.00 hrs) since the numbers of auto-graphic recording rain gauges giving depth duration figures of storm rainfall remains quite small. There were 151 occasions on which 125 mm or more precipitation was recorded during the rainfall day in the period 1863–1970 (Bleasdale 1970) in the UK. Over 70% of such falls occurred in the upland areas of the Western Highlands of Scotland, the Lake District, Snowdonia, upland South Wales and the moors of South West England, and winter was found to be the main season for such falls. There are very few districts where a fall of 100 mm of rain or more in a day has not been recorded in the last 100 years. Of interest are the widespread falls of 150 mm or more in the two lowland areas of Somerset and Dorset, and the area from Norfolk up the east coast to northern Scotland. The fall of 280 mm on 18 July 1955 at Martinstown near Dorchester in Dorset, remains the largest 24-hour fall on record in the British Isles, although it

Table 4.2 The largest daily falls of rain on record in the UK.

Date	Place and county	Total fall (mm)
18 July 1955	Martinstown, Dorset	297·4
28 June 1917	Bruton, Somerset	242·8
18 August 1924	Cannington, Somerset	238·8
17 January 1974	Sloy Main Adit, near Loch Lomond, Strathclyde	238·4

Table 4.3   Largest 24-hour rainfalls on record and areas covered by heavy rainfall on one rainfall day (based on Grindley 1969).

Date	Largest 24-hr fall recorded (mm)	Rainfall in mm more than:					
		254	228	203	178	152	127
26 August 1912					54·4	691	1865
11 October 1916				25·9	103·6	531	1036
28 June 1917	241		5·2	33·6	75·1	220	745
18 August 1924	238		2·6	7·8	12·9	18·1	26
12 August 1948						20·7	337
15 August 1952	228			44		109	
18 July 1955	279	36·3	72·5	124·3	215	345	505
10 July 1968						82·9	533

All areas shown are in square kilometres.

is of interest to note that flooding on this occasion was not severe, since the underlying chalk was able to absorb large quantities of water and then release it over an extended period of time. Other severe rainstorms occurring in South West England dominate the table of the largest 24–hour falls on record (Table 4.2), and we may conclude that this part of the country is susceptible to occasional heavy summer thunderstorm rainfall. The areas covered by heavy rainfall in one day is often quite small, as can be seen in Table 4.3. Work on the magnitude of the greatest daily rainfall in Ireland suggests a complex pattern with the southern counties more likely to be affected. The largest fall noted to date in 24 hours is 184 mm in County Dublin on 11 June 1963.

Although the lower evaporation rates of winter can cause more extensive saturation of catchments after heavy rainfall it is interesting to see from Table 4.4 that a majority of the floods documented in scientific papers in the UK since 1829 have occurred during the summer months. Characteristically such floods are the result of extremely localised short–duration convective precipitation often associated with thunderstorms. As much as 20% of the average annual precipitation has been noted in one day in parts of South East England. Summer flood severity can be particularly damaging if an orographic component is present allowing lifting of moist air, while steep catchments promote rapid discharges. The Lynmouth floods of 15 August 1952 provide a classic and well–documented (Bleasdale & Douglas 1952, Bonacina 1952, Kidson 1953) example of such circumstances and resulted in 34 deaths and the virtual destruction of the town of Lynmouth. It has been suggested that on this occasion the non–orographic component of precipitation was less than half the total of 229 mm recorded on upland Exmoor. Severe storms over the Mendip hills on 10 July 1968 have been described by Hanwell and Newson (1970) who have emphasised the importance of the topography in increasing the rainfall on this occasion too.

There is evidence that the occurrence frequency of heavy rainfall may also be greater over urban areas as a result of increased roughness, the role of pollutants in providing condensation nucleii, and more active thermals as a result of the urban heat island. Detailed analysis of a thunderstorm on 21 August 1959 which gave falls of over 50 mm in central London, very strongly suggests that the heat island had a real influence on storm initiation (Atkinson 1970). Northwest London experienced a remarkably intense rainstorm on 14 August 1975 when in a period of about 3 hours 171 mm of rain fell at Hampstead and damage estimated at over £1 million was reported (Keers & Wescott 1976). This was an isolated severe storm, probably the result of excessive diurnal heating of unstable moist air over London with the local topography influencing the precise location of the storm. A wide variety of synoptic situations can produce the unstable atmosphere and deep convection necessary to allow heavy thundery summer rainfall. Frequently small and rather shallow depressions often moving from the Bay of Biscay up the English Channel or across southern England have been responsible for major flood situations. The synoptic charts for the day of the Lynmouth flood and for 15 September 1968, when major flooding affected Surrey and Kent are shown in Figure 4.1. A pronounced convergence zone in the lower troposphere which remained quasi-stationary led to the dumping of a heavy fall of rain over a relatively small area on the latter occasion.

Extensive river floodplain inundation is more characteristic of winter cyclonic storm flooding, occasioned by persistent or recurrent precipitation (multiple-event floods). The Severn, Exe, Avon, Thames, Trent and Yorkshire Ouse are among the rivers that are particularly vulnerable, and one of the most severe examples of such flooding affected Exeter and Exmouth during the autumn of 1960, when during a ten-week period five serious floods inundated the lower part of the Exe valley affecting 3000 houses. The rainfall intensities and storm

Figure 4.1 Synoptic charts for 15 August 1952 and 15 September 1968.

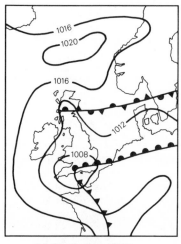
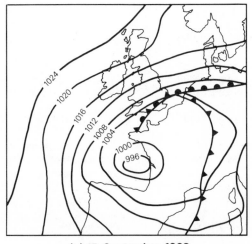

(a) 15 August 1952   **(b) 15 September 1968**

Table 4.4 A sample of documented floods in the United Kingdom since 1829 (partly after Newson 1975).

Date of flood	Area/rivers affected	Author of paper	Journal/publishers
August 1829	Moray	Sir Thomas Dick Lauder	Black, Edinburgh, 1830
January 1841	(S)Wiltshire (R. Till)	D. E. Cross	*Weather,* 1967
*November 1894	Thames	G. J. Symons and G. Chatterton	*Q. J. R. Meteorol. Soc.,* 1895
*November 1894	W. Midlands/S.W. England	A. Southall	*Q. J. R. Meteorol. Soc.,* 1895
February 1897	Bath (R. Avon)	Reporters/ correspondents	*Keenes Bath Journal*
August 1912	Norwich and E. Anglia	anon	*British rainfall,* 1912
August 1912	Norwich and E. Anglia	R. E. Pestell	*Norfolk Fair,* 1970
June 1917	Bruton (Somerset)	anon	*British rainfall,* 1917
August 1917	N. Dartmoor	R. Hansford	*Trans Dev. Ass.,* 1930
May 1920	Louth (Lincs.)	P. M. Crosthwaite	*Trans Wat. Engng,* 1921
August 1924	N. Somerset	J. Glasspoole	*British rainfall,* 1924
June 1930	Stainmore (Westmoreland)	F. Huddleston	*British rainfall,* 1930
July 1930	N.E. Yorks. (R. Esk)	English *et al.*	Whitby Lit./Phil. Soc.
June 1931	Bootle (Cumberland)	anon	*British rainfall,* 1931
November 1931	S. Wales	Pontypool R.D.C.	The Griffin Press, 1935
May 1936	Chilterns (Bucks)	K. P. Oakley	Records of Bucks, 1945
January 1939	Ipswich (R. Gipping)	Reporters	*East Anglian Daily Times,* 1939
May 1944	Central/W. Wales	A. A. Miller	*Weather,* 1951
March 1947	(S)Midlands and South	B. Howarth *et al.*	*J. Inst. Wat. Engrs,* 1948
November 1947	(S)Inverness-shire	P. O. Wolf	*J. Inst. Wat. Engrs,* 1952
August 1948	S.E. Scotland	G. Baxter	*J. Inst. Wat. Engrs,* 1949
August 1948	S.E. Scotland	A. T. A. Learmonth	*Scottish Geogl Mag.,* 1950
August 1948	S.E. Scotland	J. Glasspoole and C. K. M. Douglas	*Meteorol. Mag.,* 1949
August 1948	S.E. Scotland	A. Scott	*Scottish Agriculture,* 1950
August 1952	Lynmouth (N. Devon)	C. H. Dobbie and P. O. Wolf	*Proc. Inst. Civ. Engrs,* 1953
August 1952	Lynmouth (N. Devon)	G. W. Green	*Bull. Geol. Surv.,* 1955
August 1952	Lynmouth (N. Devon)	P. Browne	*Readers' Digest,* 1972
August 1952	Lynmouth (N. Devon)	C. Kidson and J. Gifford	*Geography,* 1953
August 1952	Lynmouth (N. Devon)	A. Bleasdale and C. K. M. Douglas	*Meteorol. Mag.,* 1952
August 1952	Lynmouth (N. Devon)	W. N. McClean	*J. Inst. Wat. Engrs,* 1953
May 1953	Lochaber, Appin, Benderlock	R. Common	*Scottish Geogl Mag.,* 1954
August 1954	S. Wales	G. M. Howe	*Meteorol. Mag.,* 1955
July 1955	Weymouth	W. J. Arkell	*Proc. Dorset Nat. Hist./ Arch. Soc.,* 1955
July 1955	Weymouth	D. J. Paxman	*Proc. Dorset Nat. Hist./ Arch. Soc.,* 1955

Date of flood	Area/rivers affected	Author of paper	Journal/publishers
August 1956	Moray	F. H. W. Green	*Scottish Geogl Mag.,* 1958
August 1956	Cairngorms	P. D. Baird and W. V. Lewis	*Scottish Geogl Mag.,* 1958
October 1956	Border areas	R. Common	*Scottish Geogl Mag.,* 1958
August 1957	W. Derbyshire	F. A. Barnes and H. R. Potter	*E. Midland Geogrs,* 1958
*December 1960	Exeter	J. Brierley	*Proc. Inst. Civ. Engrs,* 1964 (Discussion) 1965
*December 1960	West Country and S. Wales	Surface Water Survey	*J. Inst. Wat. Engrs,* 1961
*December 1960	Exmouth	A. J. M. Harrison	*The Surveyor,* 1961
*December 1960	S. Wales	G. Mcleod	Inst. Civ. Engrs, 1970
November–December 1965	S. Wales	G. Mcleod	Inst. Civ. Engrs, 1970
December 1966	Glan and Shin (W. Highlands of Scotland)	G. Reynolds	*Weather,* 1967
June 1967	W. Wales	N. Rutter and J. A. Taylor	*Weather,* 1968
July 1967	Oxford	D. McFarlane and C. G. Smith	*Meteorol. Mag.,* 1968
August 1967	Forest of Bowland (Lancs.)	J. A. Duckworth	*Ass. Riv. Auths. Yr. Bk.,* 1969
August 1967	Forest of Bowland (Lancs.)	F. Law	Fylde Water Board, 1968
*1967–8	Vale of York	J. Radley and C. Sims	Ebor Press, 1971
July 1968	Bristol, N. Somerset	P. R. S. Salter	*Meteorol. Mag.,* 1968
July 1968	Bristol, N. Somerset	P. R. S. Salter	*Meteorol. Mag.,* 1969
July 1968	Bristol, N. Somerset	J. D. Hanwell and M. D. Newson	Occ. Pub. Wessex C.C., 1970
September 1968	S.E. England	A. Bleasdale	*J. Inst. Wat. Engrs,* 1970
September 1968	S.E. England (Esher)	M. G. Jackson	*Weather,* 1977
August 1970	Glenburn (N. Ireland)	R. Common	*Irish Geographer,* 1971
August 1970	Moray	F. H. W. Green	*Scottish Geogl Mag.,* 1971
July 1973	Central N. England	P. A. Smithson M. J. Prior	*Weather,* 1974 *Meteorol. Mag.,* 1975
August 1973	Mid-Wales	M. D. Newson	Institute of Hydrology, 1974
August 1975	North London	J. F. Keers and P. Wescott	*Weather,* 1976
August 1977	Mid-Wales	A. J. Newson	*J. Meteorol.,* 1977
August 1977	London	C. M. Haggett	*Weather,* 1980
December 1979	South Wales	A. H. Perry	*Weather,* 1980

* Indicates that the paper contains a list of historical floods at the site.
(S) Indicates snowmelt involved.

durations on this occasion were not rare, but the saturated nature of the catchment, coupled with the persistent anomalous atmospheric circulation were the important causal factors. Three slow moving depressions with their associated fronts moved over the South West leading to the wettest October on record, with more than half the average annual amount recorded at Exeter in one

Figure 4.2   Five-year water equivalent of lying snow (mm) reduced to sea level (after Jackson 1977).

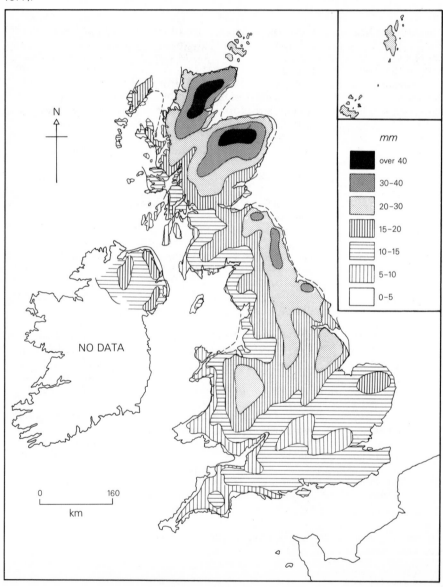

month. Severe flooding in February 1977 causing damage estimated at £1 million in Nottinghamshire accompanied precipitation totals between four and five times the February normal, caused by depressions and fronts moving slowly across central England. At least 10 deaths occurred, together with millions of pounds of damage late in December 1979 in South Wales and South West England in some of the most extensive and serious floods of recent years. Heavy rainfall on the western uplands most commonly occurs in south-westerly and westerly airstreams (Finch 1972) when depressions are moving east to the north of the country and wide warm sectors containing very moist air, which will yield abundant precipitation when forced to rise, cover the country. In the short steep catchments of the Lake District and North Wales, Holgate (1973) found that a 6 mm per hour rate of rainfall is critical for initiating flooding providing such a rate of fall is maintained for 6 hours or more.

The snowmelt contribution to floods is an important aspect of flood hydrology even though in many winters only negligible amounts of snow accumulate over most of the British Isles, and even in upland areas snow cover is not continuous. In the north of England, however, catchments draining the eastern slopes of the Pennines are subject to flooding fairly regularly, and over 16% of the gauging stations in England and Wales, and more than one-quarter in Scotland have maximum recorded floods of snowmelt origin. It is after severe winters such as 1947 and 1963 that the chance of widespread snowthaw flooding occurs. After a two-month accumulation of snow to level depths of 30 cm over wide areas in 1947, rapid thawing during early March was accompanied by heavy rainfall (itself an efficient remover of a snow cover), which in turn led to widespread, severe flooding, particularly in Fenland. In estimating potential snowmelt volumes it is necessary to know the water content of the snow which can be calculated from its depth and density. Jackson (1977a) has provided a guide of the water equivalent of lying snow, and from Figure 4.2 it can be seen that the 5-year water equivalent of lying snow at sea level ranges from less than 5 mm in the South West to over 40 mm in North East Scotland. Rapid snowmelt

Table 4.5 Station values of once in 5-year maximum 3-hour temperature with snow lying at the stations.

Station name	Altitude (m)	5-year temperature (°C)
Aberdeen	60	5·61
Acklington, Northumberland	70	5·17
Ballykelly, C. Londonderry	3	5·33
Birmingham	110	6·34
Bristol	65	4·72
Coltishall, Norfolk	15	6·02
Finningley, Yorkshire	13	5·59
Gatwick, Surrey	60	5·40
Kirkwall, Orkney	27	4·63
Nottingham	130	6·29

is usually caused by an influx of warm moist air so that air temperature provides a reasonable index of energy available for snowmelt. Table 4.5 shows the 3-hour temperature values likely to occur once in 5 years with snow lying, and from such figures estimates can be made of rare snowmelt rates.

The occurrence frequency of inland flooding is likely to be affected by changes in the frequency of heavy rainfall events. Several workers have found evidence of an increase in the frequency of heavy daily falls in recent years

Figure 4.3 Areas inundated during January 1953 floods.

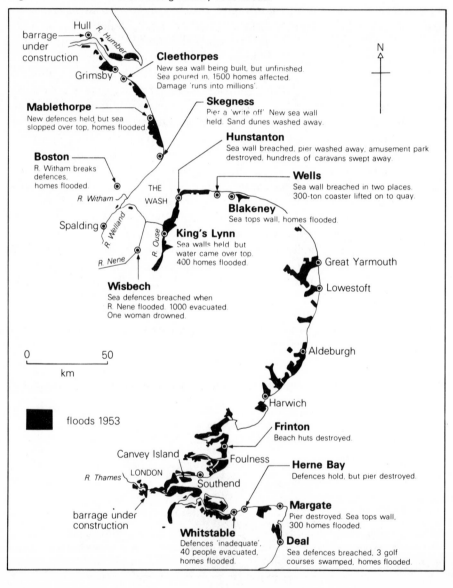

(Howe, Slaymaker & Harding 1967 – in the L. Vyrnwy area of central Wales, Rodda 1970 – at Oxford, and Finch 1972 – in Surrey). Bleasdale (1970) has noted that changing atmospheric circulation patterns over the British Isles are leading to an 'increased risk of quasi-stationary situations more favourable for the random occurrence of unusual rainfall events'. In addition there appears to be a cyclic variation in the incidence of heavy rainfall with thunderstorms bunching at certain parts of the eleven-year sunspot cycle.

Coastal flooding. The low-lying coastlands of eastern and south-eastern England are the areas most prone to coastal inundations as a result of storm surges (Perry & Walker 1977), and repeated inundations have occurred over the centuries. Historical records reveal cases from 1236 onwards and on 7 December 1663 Pepys wrote in his diary: 'there was last night the greatest tide that ever was remembered in England to have been in this river, all Whitehall having been drowned'. At least seven floods since the 13th century can be classified in the disaster category (Jensen 1953). This century disastrous flooding occurred along the Thames on 6 January 1928 drowning 14 people in London basements and leaving 4000 temporarily homeless. On 31 January 1953, there occurred what may well become known as the worst weather disaster of the century with over 800 sq. km flooded by salt water (Fig. 4.3), a total death toll of over 300 and damage estimated between £30–50 millions. Storm surges such as this in the North Sea occur when strong north-westerly and northerly winds drive water southwards into the increasingly narrow confines of the southern North Sea. If these conditions occur at time of high spring tides, then the likelihood that coastal and estuarine defences will be overtopped or structures weakened and undermined, will be much increased. Hazardous storm surges are restricted to the period September–April when large and intense depressions can generate the strong winds necessary to produce a big surge. If a surge follows a period of wet weather which will have raised river levels, the tide pushing up the estuaries of the East Coast can cause a ponding up of the fresh water coming down the rivers and enhance flooding of the low-lying estuarine lands. Large surges are only likely to occur at rare intervals when by chance a number of factors occur in a manner and with a timing which produces the maximum total effect (Summers 1978).

The storm surge of 1953 occurred when a depression developed near the Azores, deepened and moved east-north-easterly to northern Scotland and then changed direction and moved south-easterly towards Denmark. At the same time a developing anticyclone west of Ireland caused a tightening of the pressure gradient on the western flanks of the low, and geostrophic winds increased to values between 150 and 200 knots. Mean wind speeds of 70 knots with gusts of 100 knots were observed along the east coast of Scotland. It was estimated that the prolonged and violent gales had forced some 422 000 million cubic metres of water into the North Sea increasing the sea surface elevation by more than 2 m. The time at which the peak of the surge occurred varied considerably in relation to that of high water (Grieve 1959) and in the Thames estuary preceded high water by three hours. The height of the surge peak reached 3 m at Southend. Major storm surges affected the North Sea coasts in both January 1976 and 1978. On the latter occasion there was almost a major flood tragedy in London, as the waters of the Thames rose to within a few centimetres of the top of the flood defences. Gradual isostatic readjustment means that the effective tidal levels are slowly increasing over southeast England and it has been estimated that the surge with a statistical recurrence of once in 1000 years would flood about 116 sq. km of the Thames valley and directly affect some 1¼ million people (see Fig. 4.4). A fictional but nonetheless illuminating account of what could befall London has been published (Doyle 1976). South East England is tilting downwards at a rate of about 0·76 m per century and tides at London Bridge increased by 1·22 m between 1791 and 1963.

At a number of other locations flooding can follow exceptionally high tides, for example large areas of Belfast city centre are located at a very low elevation and more than 60% of the 125 recorded floods in the period 1916–72 were associated with high spring tides (Prior & Betts 1974). The combination of severe onshore gales and high tides flooded large parts of the low-lying Fylde coast of Lancashire in November 1977, causing damage estimated at more than £1 million. Perhaps the most severe flooding in these islands occurred on Severnside on 20 January 1606 when about 2000 people were drowned, as the sea defences were overtopped. A plaque on the side of Nash church, Gwent, marks the level reached by the floodwaters at the time.

Failure of manmade structures. Reservoirs impounded by dams represent a potential flood hazard despite the continuing research by civil engineers and hydrologists to ensure that design criteria are constantly modified in the light of new knowledge. Among the disasters that have occurred, the Dale Dyke dam (12 km west of Sheffield) breach of 11 March 1864 which killed 245 people and flooded 5000 buildings is perhaps the worst. In a few minutes 700 million gallons of water flooded into the valley below the dam and a flood wave then engulfed valley settlements. In November 1925 a dam disaster occurred at Dolgarrog in North Wales in which 16 people were drowned and great damage was caused in the flooded Conway valley. Boulders moved by the torrent weighed up to 100 tons and formed a fan which is still in existence. No attempt had been made to tie the dam to the solid rocks beneath the glacial drift on which it was built and the inadequate foundations were the main cause of the disaster. It emphasised the need for full site investigation prior to building and for regular inspection of reservoirs, and led to the passing in 1930 of the Reservoirs (Safety Provisions) Act. The policing and administration of the Act has not been particularly successful and since many dams are over 90 years old they were built on unsuitable sites at a time when engineering knowledge was sparse. It is quite possible that the inner cores of some of these dams are being slowly eroded by seeping water which could lead to a collapse. Canals, particularly those running through urban areas, are a possible flood hazard, especially as maintenance of canal banks has been widely neglected in recent years. In December 1978 a

Figure 4.4 An attempt to increase the public's perception of the danger to London from flooding. Posters of this kind have been widely displayed in the metropolis.

breach occurred in a section of the Coventry canal and millions of gallons of water flooded about 60 houses in the city forcing people to evacuate their homes for a time.

Flood hazard evaluation

Systematic evaluation of floods and the flood hazard by teams of workers is now beginning in the UK as evidenced by the setting up of the Flood Studies team at the Institute of Hydrology following concern over a series of major flood events in the 1960s and of the Flood Hazard Research Project at Middlesex Polytechnic. *Per capita* flood damage in England and Wales each year is on average about four times greater than in the USA. Inevitably much of the stimulus to study the hazard and to initiate flood alleviation schemes, has been the disasters that have already been mentioned in previous sections. Currently the new Water Authorities are undertaking 'section 24 surveys' (Ministry of Agriculture 1974) which

Figure 4.5 Flood marks on old buildings, like those on this parish church in King's Lynn, Norfolk, provide a valuable source of historical flood data.

will extend knowledge of the flood hazard identifying more exactly than before areas at risk and flood damage potential.

Estimates of flood frequency are required for the design and appraisal of a variety of engineering works (see Fig. 4.5). Because streamflow data is less plentiful than rainfall data, the analysis of rainfall records is basic to flood

Figure 4.6   Sixty-minute rainfall with a 5-year return period in the British Isles (after Jackson 1977).

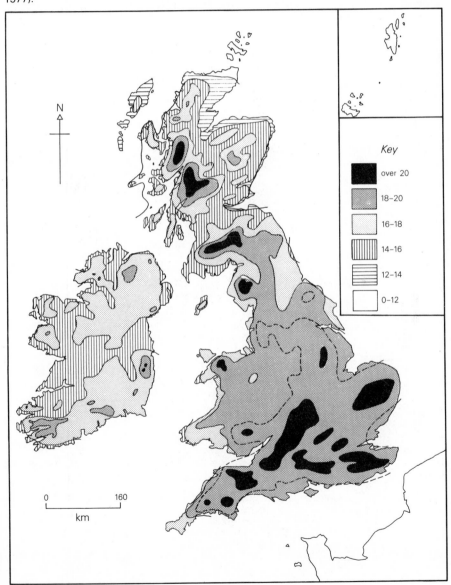

Key

■	over 20
▨	18–20
░	16–18
▥	14–16
▤	12–14
□	0–12

0   160
km

analyses (Newson 1975). To help to ascertain the frequency of heavy falls and the largest falls likely at a location, or over an area during a specified period, the statistical theory of extreme values is employed (see Chapter 1). Bilham (1935) was the first to produce a soundly based probability analysis for rainfall of durations of between 5 and 120 minutes. More recently the Flood Studies Report (1975), a monumental work which has no equal in the world, used 600 long-period raingauges, each with an average 60 years of record to produce a full

Figure 4.7   Two-day rainfall with a 5-year return period in the British Isles (after Jackson 1977).

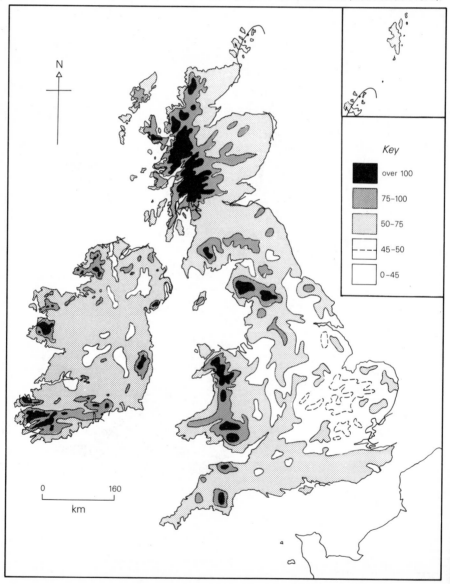

Key

over 100

75–100

50–75

45–50

0–45

range of return periods of storm rainfall of durations of 1 hour and 2 days. Figure 4.6 shows the 60-minute rainfall over the British Isles with a 5-year return period and Figure 4.7 shows for the same return period the 2-day fall. Figure 4.6 suggests that the largest predicted falls in 2 rainfall days occur in the most elevated parts of the country. Figure 4.5 shows that over the much shorter period of 60 minutes the amounts falling over parts of southern and eastern England are similar to those in western Scotland. Some comparative analysis by Kelway (1977) using the Bilham and Flood Studies equations to calculate the return period of a storm in northeast England suggests very considerable variation occurs, as can be seen in Figure 4.8. Opinion remains divided as to whether one method is more accurate than the other.

The estimation of peak flood flows from the existing flow gauge network in the British Isles is hindered by the lack of stations with a sufficiently long record. Many of the existing flow gauge stations have been established since the formation of the River Boards in 1950, and it is only since the mid-1960s that a

Figure 4.8 A comparative analysis of the return period in years of heavy rainfall in NE England on 29–30 August 1975 (after Kelway 1977).

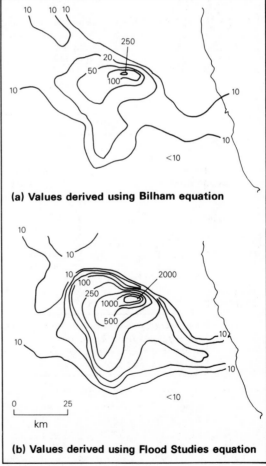

(a) Values derived using Bilham equation

(b) Values derived using Flood Studies equation

hydrometric network has been established. Because the streamflow measurement network has developed haphazardly there remains a concentration of gauging stations in the lowlands with only small numbers of high-level stations. One of the achievements of the Flood Studies Report has been the collection and listing of data from the 1100 or so river gauging stations and the extraction of flood data for fuller analysis. The information accumulated during the study forms a unique collection of flood records which, if updated at regular intervals would continue as a national archive. Frequently peak flood-flow estimates have to be based on indirect evidence such as eye-witness accounts or flood marks on

Figure 4.9 Some causes of flood intensification (after Ward 1978).

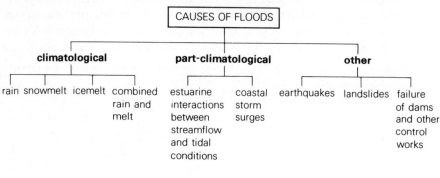

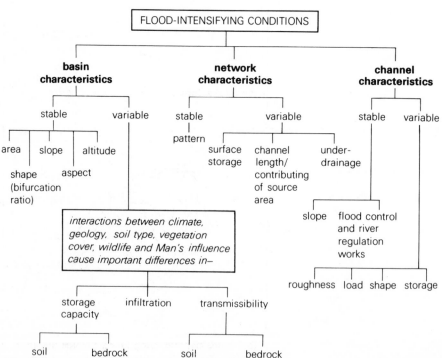

bridges, and although the assembly of historical flood records from a variety of sources is now well advanced, there must remain numerous untapped sources of semi-quantitative information in newspapers and county record offices. Where no records are available at a site a preliminary estimate may be made from the relation between floods and catchment characteristics obtained from maps. Statistical investigation of flood records have led to a number of countrywide and regional equations relating floods to catchment characteristics (Nash & Shaw 1965).

Where river flow records are too short to provide reliable estimates of floods of a very long return-period long rainfall records can be used for the simulation of big floods by means of a hydrograph model. The development of unit hydrograph techniques began in the 1930s and descriptions of the method are readily available (see Nash 1966, Newson 1975).

The character of the catchment will determine the response to heavy rainfall and in Figure 4.9 the effects of some physical catchment parameters which can lead to flood intensification are noted. The main flood-intensifying conditions can be grouped under the headings of basin network and channel characteristics, each group having some characteristics which are stable and others which are more unstable. Of the stable basin characteristics, shape is one of the most important. A compact circular catchment can lead to larger concentrated floods in the low sections. Geology, soil type and vegetation variations are especially important variable basin characteristics. Impervious catchments will produce a great amount of surface runoff, while permeable and pervious rocks have a capacity for water storage. Drainage patterns which result in the coalescence of flood flows from a number of tributaries in the lower part of the drainage basin can result in high-magnitude flood peaks at the basin outlet. The channel characteristics affect the passage of floodwater downstream, and in particular roughness of the bed and bank affect the velocity and magnitude of the flood.

Work on the human responses to floods (known by some as behavioural flood studies) represents an integral part of evaluation studies of the flood hazard. Such work has received less attention in the UK than in the USA and the first attempts to discuss the administrative, economic and social aspects of floods in England and Wales were carried out by geographers at the University of Chicago (Burton 1961). The lack of research in economic and social aspects of floods in Britain has led to glaring omissions in our knowledge of the flood hazard, and our ability to manage floodplain resources effectively. Apart from a relatively few local case studies there is a general non-availability of data on flood effects. A striking imbalance exists between, on the one hand hydrological and meteorological data, and on the other economic and social data. A second area of flood hazard research which has almost been completely neglected by British geographers, engineers and planners alike, is that of influencing human behaviour in order to attain specific management objectives.

From an economic point of view flooding can be regarded as a kind of tax exacted by nature and central to the economic study of floods is the need for systematic collection and storage of information on flood damage (Parker &

Penning-Rowsell 1972). There are two basic approaches to the assessment of flood damages:

(a)   The collection of information on damages as they occur. Surveys are best carried out in the early post-flood period and can include the use of questionnaires, flood insurance premium information, aerial photography and fire brigade records of pumped out premises.

(b)   A theoretically based approach which involves costing likely damage from flood events drawing on the accumulation of experience of flood damage from many events.

Figure 4.10   Residential depth-damage information. (a) Basic data sets; (b) damage components; (c) flood duration; (d) flood warning.

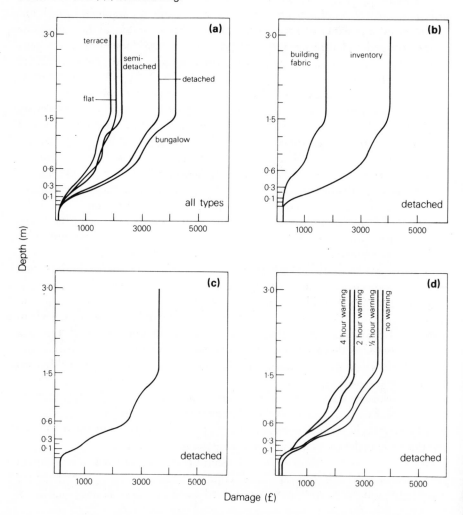

The second approach was developed in the USA and is now being applied in Britain (Chatterton 1978). White introduced the concept of the depth–damage curve to relate potential damage in a property to depth of flooding. Different types of property will be affected differently and some examples of standard residential depth–damage information is shown in Figure 4.10. Despite similarity of shape, the curves show a considerable range of maximum damage potential although in each case there is a tailing off of the increase in damage with floods greater than about 1·5 m. For an area results can be aggregated to provide estimates of potential losses which would be produced by various levels of floods.

In reality, of course, damage is a function of not only depth but also flood water velocity, effluent content, flood duration and many other variables (see Fig. 4.11). Conceivably such information might be used to prepare scenarios of future disasters, and to provide answers to questions like what would be the result of a 175 mm rainfall in 24 hours in a particular catchment? Results from investigations of flood damage can be used to provide cost–benefit information for intended flood alleviation schemes for as Parker (1973) points out 'information on the costs of flooding is a basic prerequisite for sound planning for flood hazard reduction'.

Figure 4.11 The depth and duration of flooding are two of the parameters that determine the cost and extent of damage. For the old and infirm, being rescued by boat can be just one aspect of a terrifying ordeal.

Recently the application of social survey techniques has allowed perception of the flood hazard to be appraised and an evaluation made of the annoyance, inconvenience and worry suffered by the people who experience flooding. Studies of flood hazard awareness at Shrewsbury (Harding & Parker 1974) suggest that significant numbers of floodplain inhabitants consistently underestimate the flood risk. Of 132 householders interviewed who lived within the area inundated by the highest flood on record, only 45% replied positively to the question 'is there a flood problem in this area?'. Such a low level of awareness implies that few individuals will plan for future floods. The recency and frequency of personal experience of flooding and perhaps personality traits are important factors in explaining flood hazard perception. Infrequent hazards such as floods are typically soon forgotten by most people and this must be the cause for some concern. In many cases the flood hazard is ignored or minimised by floodplain dwellers and the inhabitants of flood-prone coastal strips despite the opinions of technical experts, or even despite repeated flood experience.

Flood hazard reduction

In such densely populated countries as the UK it is hardly feasible to leave land unused just because it is subject to periodic inundation, especially as flood-prone land is often fertile and reasonably flat. So that the community may benefit from its economic advantages, ways must be found to use this land, but to achieve economic optimisation the flood hazard cannot be ignored and ways must be found to accommodate it. Although loss bearing by floodplain occupants is a course of action which exists, it is usually more appropriate to consider a number of possible remedial measures which may be adopted to reduce vulnerability to the flood hazard.

The construction of appropriate engineering works such as widened and excavated channels, relief channels, embankments and regulating reservoirs offers a frequently costly, structural adjustment to the hazard. One point about such adjustments, which has been clearly illustrated in the American literature, is that they can lead to the development of an attitude that the flood hazard has been totally eliminated, particularly as much publicity is frequently given to expensive large-scale engineering work. Should a really rare flood of high recurrence interval occur, catastrophic flood losses could result. Flood storage areas have been constructed to serve as temporary storage reservoirs for the control of flood flows and are often located in or near towns and cities. At Basildon, Essex, for example, a site of 100 acres provides flood storage from a catchment of over 1000 impermeable acres, and is designed to cope with a 1 in 10 year storm. Obviously the design of such structures is the province of the civil engineer, but the environmental scientist can help in researching methods of assessing the benefits to be obtained from flood alleviation projects. One of the most expensive protective schemes yet undertaken involves the construction of a movable barrier across the R. Thames at Woolwich to effectively isolate

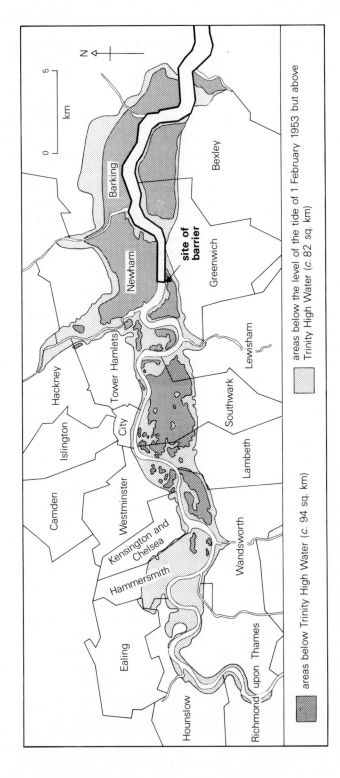

Figure 4.12 Areas of London liable to inundation by flooding.

London from the sea tide if flooding appears likely and safeguard the lives and homes of more than a million people in some 130 square kilometres of Greater London (see Fig. 4.12). The completion of this major scheme has now been delayed until the early 1980s. The importance of it has been highlighted by the remarks of the chairman of the Greater London Council Recreation and Community Services Policy Committee 'if a huge tidal surge came up the Thames without the barrier it could be the greatest natural disaster this country has experienced, and a catastrophe for the capital on the scale of the Great Fire of London, some £3000 millions of damage could be caused and the seat of government forced away from London'. When not in use the barrier gates will rest out of sight in the river bed allowing free passage of river traffic through the openings between the piers. Since the barrier will raise water levels on the seaward side a programme of bank-raising downriver has also been necessary. One major factor which was taken into account when the desirability of building the barrier was being considered, was the need to maintain the beauty of London's riverline for the thousands of tourists who visit the capital every year. If the traditional solution of raising and strengthening river walls and embankments had been adopted there would have been an amenity loss to riverside areas. The Institute of Oceanographic Science has simulated the 1953 surge, using a specially formulated numerical model. Predicted water levels can be compared with observed values and useful results for the operation of the future Thames barrier have been obtained.

While there is a tendency for the water engineer concerned with flood loss reduction to think in terms of engineering solutions to flood problems, such proposals may not always be possible or feasible. In such cases loss reduction may be based on non-structural measures such as flood forecasting, and flood-warning or alert schemes. Smith (1972) points out, most forecasting techniques depend on the interpretation of present events in the light of previous catchment responses to both analogous situations and antecedent conditions over the drainage basin. Heavy rainfall warnings are issued by the Meteorological Office based on research into the structure and mechanisms of rainfall systems, together with measurements of rainfall using radar systems. The Dee Valley weather radar project (Harrold *et al.* 1973) has shown how it is possible to forecast rainfall quantitatively for some hours ahead, while work at the Meteorological Office with a 10-level numerical model allows predictions of frontal rainfall over periods of up to 36 hours. The Greater London Council has announced it is to use radar to help give more reliable and speedier warning of flooding from London's small rivers, which can occur within half an hour from the onset of heavy rain. This follows 25 flooding incidents in the years 1965–76 as the result of the overflow of non-tidal rivers in the London area. Flood forecasting and warning systems have evolved into a highly sophisticated alleviative measure and Porter (1978) noted that by 1970 15 river authorities had implemented some form of system.

A typical example of river flood warning system is that used at Shrewsbury (Harding & Parker 1974). Responsibility for issuing a warning rests with the

Severn Trent Water Authority which is usually able to give 24–36 hours warning of a flood. As soon as a flood warning is received a control centre is set up and flood wardens notify householders likely to be affected. As a model of what is needed for planned anticipation of natural hazards, the London Flood Control Centre and the associated Storm Tide Warning Service provide a good example. There are three stages in the warning system:

(1) An alert can be given of potential danger 12 hours before high water, based on weather conditions and the build up of any surges along the East Coast.

(2) An 'alert confirmed' or cancellation is issued 4 hours before high water and the London Flood Room is manned by river engineers. An hour later warnings and advice would be broadcast on radio and TV.

(3) A danger message to police and river authorities to activate a warning system when the tide is approaching danger level. Air raid sirens would be sounded and public transport withdrawn from the risk area.

A number of test trials of the system and the complex administrative command structure involved have been carried out to perfect the overall operation. A massive publicity campaign has been launched to inform Londoners of the arrangements so that not only people living in the risk area, but also the million or so daily commuters are familiar with the arrangements. When the Thames barrier is completed the Storm Tide Warning Service will still be required, and will send alerts directly to the barrier control building, where engineers will decide whether closure is necessary, and if so the optimum time to close the gates. In 1978 a West Coast storm warning system was established, known as Neptune, with headquarters at the North West Water Authority.

In practice flood forecasting and structural protection schemes are combined in many catchments. The Bristol Avon catchment covers an area of 2200 sq. km with a mean annual rainfall of 860 mm and is roughly circular in shape. A number of urban areas with a potential flood risk are situated in the catchment. At Bath for example, more than 20 floods have occurred since 1880, and following the major floods of 1960, a comprehensive improvement of the Avon through the city has been carried out. Vertical channel banks were constructed to obtain the maximum channel capacity, the channel was realigned in places, old bridges replaced and automatic sluices added which would allow a temporarily wider channel for flood flows (Newson 1975). The rain storms and floods of summer 1968 highlighted the need for comprehensive flood forecasting, and the warning system which is now in operation is based on information from:

(a) the forecasts and rainfall warnings of the Meteorological Office;

(b) direct observations by key rainfall observers in the catchment;

(c) interrogation over GPO lines of automatic rain gauges and river level stations. Radio links rather than telephone lines are becoming a common source of communication between gauging stations and flood headquarters.

The latter telemetry system is able to provide data from over 30 out-stations at a central point where it can be computer handled and fed into a forecasting model, which will predict flow and water levels at a number of locations. Results are required very rapidly especially in the case of flash floods which can result from extremely localised heavy rainfall in the catchment. Because of the catchment characteristics the time available for warning, and if necessary evacuating river-side properties under such circumstances is very short. A sophisticated system of this type allows a much greater reliability and accuracy of flood forecasting. The system allows two levels of warning – a preliminary standby, essentially to the police, and the main warning.

A possible adjustment which has been the subject of much discussion is land-use development control. Land should be developed according to its vulnerability to floods, but the spread of floodplain occupance with an encroach-ment of housing and industry is a feature of the changing land-use pattern in many parts of the British Isles. Urbanisation modifies the nature of the flood hazard by introducing impermeable surfaces, storm sewers and drains which allow a rapid rate of runoff. A study of a catchment in Essex which between 1953 and 1968 became one-quarter covered by urban development suggested that summer and autumn discharges increased five-fold. The increase in flood potential may not be constant for each rainfall event, but may vary with storm characteristics and antecedent conditions (Packman 1979). It appears that small frequent floods increase in frequency although large rare floods that are likely to cause severe damage are not significantly affected by the construction of urban areas within the catchment (Hollis 1975). In the area of the Welsh Borderland shown on Figure 4.13 over 7000 urban properties are at risk. The spread of building on to the floodplain of the river Trent at Nottingham has been described by Nixon (1963) and Figure 4.14 shows a similar process at Gloucester with considerable late-nineteenth- and early-twentieth-century building. Improved floodplain management and the designation of areas of flood risk is needed. In the past there has been a tendency to 'solve' flood problems as they arise rather than to undertake flood prevention in anticipation of the event. The designation of flood risk areas is needed, followed by statutory imposition of strict controls on development by the local planning authority. Management techniques such as floodplain zoning, widely practised in the USA (Kates and White 1961) would designate areas of prohibitive and restrictive development allowing low-damage-potential land use like sports grounds but not residential development in flood-prone areas. As Penning-Rowsell and Parker (1973) point out – 'a policy which realises the true costs and benefits of floodplain develop-ment linked to an extension of the principle of grant-aiding of flood alleviation measures for areas of existing floodplain development would result in a wiser use and control of floodplains than is currently the case'. The main problem with a zoning policy is the length of time needed to effect action in an already developed area. Zoning is a long-term solution, but great opportunities are presented as urban renewal takes place. Flood alleviation schemes allow a more diverse and intensive use of land formerly subject to frequent flooding by

Figure 4.13 Welsh Borderland areas susceptible to flooding.

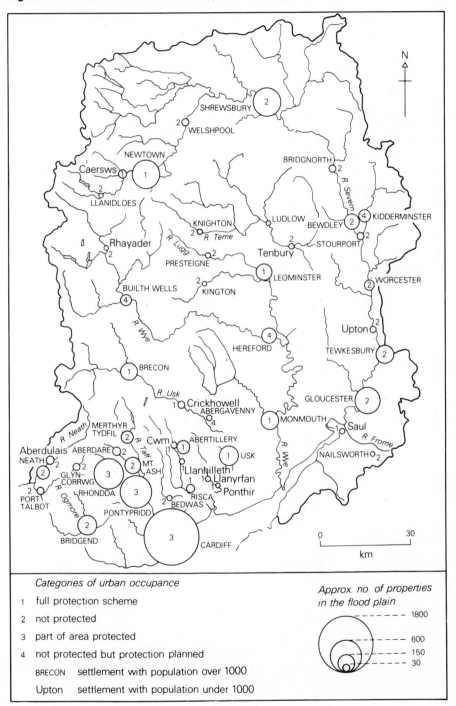

Categories of urban occupance

1   full protection scheme

2   not protected

3   part of area protected

4   not protected but protection planned

BRECON   settlement with population over 1000

Upton   settlement with population under 1000

Approx. no. of properties
in the flood plain

------- 1800

------- 600

------- 150

------- 30

reducing the flood hazard, and the enhanced value of the protected land is a major benefit. Examination of old maps frequently reveals that our forebears avoided settlements in floodplains but modern man has often been less prudent. Protection of individual buildings is possible with structural alterations. At Shrewsbury redevelopment of flood-prone areas has involved property elevation with floor levels constructed above the level of the highest recorded flood.

Preceding paragraphs have mainly dealt with community adjustments to flooding involving collective action by institutions and groups of individuals, but individual adjustments made on the initiative of individual floodplain dwellers also take place. Adjustments requiring short-term planning include sandbagging and the moving of furniture upstairs, while insurance is an example of longer-term planning. In the Shrewsbury study (Harding & Parker 1974) a minority of residents were found to have flood insurance cover, and the possibility of obtaining flood insurance in high risk areas varied from company to company. As in other parts of the country the basis for flood insurance is entirely satisfactory from the insurance company's standpoint because blanket premiums are adjusted in the long term to recover payments made to claimants. From the householder's standpoint, should he wish to obtain flood insurance the basis for premium calculation tends to be rather unsatisfactory because premiums are not sensitive to local variations in risk. The following figures indicate typical losses borne by the insurance companies in the past:

Figure 4.14   The development of urban growth at Gloucester.

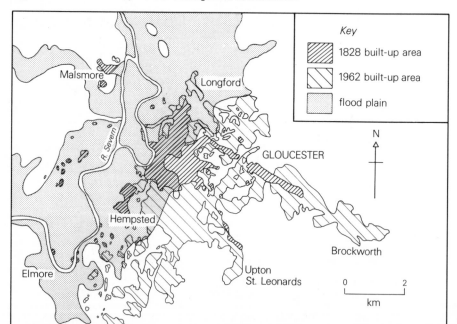

	Actual damage	Estimated insurance paid
East Coast coastal floods	£30–50 millions	£6½ millions
West Country 1960	£10–11 millions	£6 millions
Widespread floods 1968	£5–6 millions	£3 millions

In any large flood disaster publicity is given to the collection of money for public relief. Relief funds are normally set up for humanitarian reasons to relieve hardship and aid rehabilitation and recovery. Average reimbursements from such funds varied from 4–26% during floods in the 1960s. It can be argued that the whole notion of compensating hazard victims from their losses reflects an ambiguity of public attitude since it apparently protects the individual from the adverse effects of his decision to take risks. Although disaster funds are normally set up for admirable reasons they can result in a situation whereby householders in low risk areas pay for their own insurance whereas those who choose to invest in a high risk area may remain uninsured but receive compensation when damage occurs. The Lynmouth Flood Disaster Fund, set up following wide-spread publicity of the disaster, raised £2 millions which provided adequate compensation and financed the construction of a flood alleviation scheme. Anxiety, ill-health and tension often manifest themselves in a community after the period of extreme emergency has passed and during the repair period, and there are several examples of community grumbling about the attitudes of officials and the distribution of relief funds. Government aid may be available after floods, as in the case of the 1978 East Coast floods where the government promised councils that they would pay 75% of any spending which exceeded the product of a penny rate. The European Economic Community's social fund can be allocated to a disaster area, normally to undertake emergency repairs, for example to sea defences.

Conclusions

Although there is a long tradition of coping with floods in the British Isles and planning the use of land based on a common sense approach, more work is needed on identifying the distribution, extent and severity of the flood hazard. This hazard remains a serious, recurrent and widespread problem and the potential for flood hazard reduction measures is high. Studies of the hazard comprise many threads – knowledge of the natural mechanisms of floods, an understanding of human behaviour and decision-making in the flood–risk environment, and an awareness of the realities and constraints of the political process – to name but a few. Further research is particularly required to prescribe optimum adjustments for a given flood hazard situation. The British literature has been dominated by studies of the physical hydrology of floods and their alleviation by engineering remedies, but there are now welcome signs that work is developing on a fully integrated approach to floodplain management, includ-ing the evaluation of social and economic criteria.

Bibliography

Atkinson, B. W. 1970. *The reality of the urban effect on precipitation – a case study.* World Meteorol. Org. Tech. Note 108, 343–59. Geneva: World Meteorol. Org.

Bilham, E. G. 1935. Classification of heavy falls of rain in short periods. *British rainfall.* London: HMSO.

Bleasdale, A. 1970. The rainfall of 14–15 September 1968 in comparison with previous exceptional rainfall in the UK. *J. Inst. Wat. Engrs* **24**, 181–9.

Bleasdale, A. and C. K. M. Douglas 1952. Storm over Exmoor on 15 August 1952. *Weather* **24**, 363–9.

Bonacina, L. C. W. 1952. The Exmoor cataclysm. *Weather* **7**, 336–8.

Brierley, J. 1964. Flooding in the Exe valley 1960. *Proc. Inst. Civ. Engrs* **28**, 151–70.

Burton, I. 1961. Some aspects of flood loss reduction in England and Wales. In *Papers on flood problems,* G. F. White (ed.). Res. Paper, no. 115. Chicago: Dept of Geography, Univ. of Chicago.

Chatterton, J. B. 1978. The benefits of flood alleviation – an evaluation of assessment techniques in the UK. *Water Services* **82**, 89–96.

Cole, G. 1972. The East Coast and London tidal flood warning system. *Phil. Trans R. Soc. Lond. A* **272**, 173–8.

Doyle, R. 1976. *Deluge.* London: Arlington Books Ltd.

Finch, C. R. 1972. Some heavy rainfalls in Great Britain 1956–71. *Weather* **27**, 364–77.

Grieve, H. 1959. *The great tide.* Chelmsford: Essex Co. Council.

Grindley, J. 1969. Some highlights of 1968 rainfall over Britain. *Weather* **24**, 363–9.

Hanwell, J. D. and M. D. Newson 1970. *The great storms and floods of July 1968 on the Mendips.* Wessex Cave Club Occ. Paper, no. 8. Bristol: Wessex Cave Club.

Harding, D. M. and E. A. Porter 1969. *Flood loss information and economic aspects of floodplain occupance.* Hydrol. Group Informal Disc., 403–9. London: Inst. of Civ. Engineers.

Harding, D. M. and D. J. Parker 1974. Flood hazard at Shrewsbury in the UK. In *Natural hazards, local, national and global,* G. F. White (ed.), 43–52. New York: Oxford University Press.

Harrison, A. J. M. 1961. The 1960 Exmouth floods. *The Surveyor* **120**, 127–32.

Harrold, T. W. 1973. Mechanisms influencing the distribution of precipitation within baroclinic disturbances. *Q. J. R. Meteorol. Soc.* **99**, 232–51.

Hewitt, K. and I. Burton 1971. *The hazardousness of a place.* Research Publication, no. 6. Toronto: Dept of Geography, Univ. of Toronto.

Holgate, H. T. D. 1973. Rainfall forecasting for river authorities. *Meteorol. Mag.* **102**, 33–48.

Hollis, G. E. 1975. The effect of urbanisation on flooding of different recurrence intervals. *Water Resources Res.* **11**, 431–5.

Howe, G. M., H. Slaymaker and D. M. Harding 1967. Some aspects of the flood hydrology of the upper catchments of the Severn and Wye. *Trans Inst. Br. Geogrs* **41**, 35–58.

Jackson, M. C. 1977a. The water equivalent of lying snow. *J. Inst. Water Engrs Scient.* **31**, 54–6.

Jackson, M. C. 1977b. Evaluating the probability of heavy rain. *Meteorol. Mag.* **106**, 185–92.

Jensen, H. A. P. 1953. Tidal inundations past and present. *Weather* **8**, 85–9 and 108–12.

Kates, R. W. and G. F. White 1961. Flood hazard evaluation. In *Papers on flood problems*, G. F. White (ed.), 135–47. Res. Paper, no. 70. Chicago: Univ. of Chicago.

Keers, J. F. and P. Wescott 1976. The Hampstead storm – 14 August 1975. *Weather* **31**, 2–10.

Kelway, P. S. 1977. Characteristics of rainfall conditions with particular reference to NE England. *J. Inst. Water Engrs Scient.* **31**, 251–68.

Kidson, C. 1953. The Exmoor storm and the Lynmouth floods. *Geography* **38**, 1–9.

Logue, J. J. 1975. *Extreme rainfalls in Ireland*. Tech. Note, no. 40. Dublin: Met. Office.

Ministry of Agriculture, Fisheries and Food 1974.*Guidance notes for Water Authorities*. Mem. Water Act 1973, Section 24. London: MAFF.

Nash, J. E. 1966. Applied flood hydrology. In *River engineering and water conservation works*, R. B. Thorn (ed.). London: Butterworth.

Nash, J. E. and B. L. Shaw 1965. Flood frequency as a function of catchment characteristics. In *River Flood Hydrology*, 115–36. London: ICE Symposium.

NERC 1975. *Flood studies report*. London: NERC. 5 vols.

Newson, M. D. 1975. *Flooding and the flood hazard in the UK*. Oxford: Oxford University Press.

Nixon, M. 1963. *Flood regulation and river training in England and Wales*. Conservation of Water Res., 137–50. London: Inst. of Civil Engrs.

Packman, J. C. 1979. The effect of urbanisation on flood magnitude and frequency. In *Man's impact on the hydrological cycle*, Hollis (ed.), 153–72. Norwich: Geo Books.

Parker, D. J. 1973. The assessment of flood damage. In *Proc. of a symposium on economic aspects of floods*, 9–20. London: Middlesex Polytechnic.

Parker, D. J. and E. Penning-Rowsell 1972. *Problems and methods of flood damage assessment*. Flood Hazard Res. Proj. Prog. Rept, no. 3. London: Middlesex Polytechnic.

Penning-Rowsell, E. and L. Underwood 1972. *Flood hazard and floodplain management – survey of existing studies*. Flood Hazard Res. Proj. Prog. Rept, no. 2. London: Middlesex Polytechnic.

Penning-Rowsell, E. and D. J. Parker 1973. *The control of floodplain development – a preliminary analysis*. Flood Hazard Res. Proj. Prog. Rept, no. 4. London: Middlesex Polytechnic.

Perry, A. H. and J. M. Walker 1977. *The ocean–atmosphere system*. London: Longman.

Porter, E. 1978. *Water management in England and Wales*. Cambridge: Cambridge University Press.

Prior, D. B. and N. I. Betts 1974. Flooding in Belfast. *Irish Geography* **7**, 1–18.

Rodda, J. C. 1970. Rainfall excesses in the United Kingdom. *Trans Inst. Br. Geogrs* **49**, 49–60.

Smith, K. 1972. *Water in Britain, a study in applied hydrology and resource geography*. London: Macmillan.

Smith, K. and G. A. Tobin 1979. *Human adjustment to the flood hazard*. London: Longman.

Summers, D. 1978. *The East Coast floods*. Newton Abbot: David and Charles.

Ward, R. 1978. *Floods*. London: Macmillan.

White, G. F. 1964. *Choice of adjustment to floods*. Res. Paper, no. 93. Chicago: Dept of Geog., Univ. of Chicago.

5 *The drought hazard*

'Thousands have lived without love, not one without water'
W. H. Auden

Introduction

Had this chapter been written before 1975–6 it would undoubtedly have been quite brief and indeed consideration would have had to be given as to whether drought in the British Isles constituted a serious hazard. The 1975–6 drought changed all this, and has been described variously as 'the greatest natural disaster to have hit the UK in modern times' (Mortimore 1976) and 'the costliest drought ever in Britain . . . it may yet prove to be the gravest economical natural disaster of all time' (Meaden 1976). Not surprisingly, a large number of articles have been written about particular aspects of the drought but probably the most comprehensive description is contained in the Institute of British Geographers' *Atlas of the drought* by Gregory and Doornkamp (1980); probably the world's first systematic atlas study of the nature, incidence and effects of a natural hazard.

Droughts are not sudden emergencies with little or no warning, as is often the case with such hazards as floods, and in general they can be defined only when they are well underway. The population needs water to arrest its thirst and to water its crops, but present–day inhabitants of the British Isles also require water on a vast and complex scale to operate effectively the intricate machinery of a highly technological society. Thus a drought is potentially a serious threat to economic activity. It can extend beyond the question of water supply to embrace such diverse fields as amenity and recreation, agriculture and industry. Droughts are natural events but water shortages result from inadequacies in facilities. Water consumption per head of population has now reached about 60 gallons per day and it has been suggested that the long–term solution to periods of water shortage is to build more reservoirs and to provide some kind of water grid to link one area of the country to another. The cost of implementing such schemes would be enormous and it is questioned whether heavy expenditure to guard against a situation which arises infrequently can be justified. It needs to be remembered that projects to regulate and restructure water movements, and thus to offset the effects of drought, represent a kind of tax levied by the drought potential of the environment.

Drought should be defined in terms of the relationship between the natural-event system and the human–use system; the unexpected deficiencies in the moisture supply from the meteorological and hydrological systems of the environment as compared with the demands of the human resource-use in that environment. Naturally different types of resource-use will have different deficiency thresholds. Drought can be defined objectively in numerous ways to suit particular purposes and Tabony (1977) has presented arguments for the use of indices which differentiate between meteorological, hydrological and agricultural drought. Whatever objective indices are used to classify droughts the root cause of drought is a rainfall deficiency of considerable duration, and Hewitt and Burton (1971) have suggested we define the drought hazard as 'a period in which moisture availability falls below the current requirements of

Figure 5.1 The regional distribution of mean annual absolute drought (after Glasspoole & Rowsell 1947).

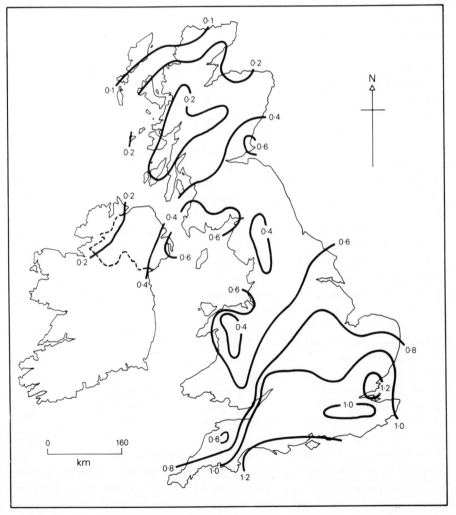

some or all the living communities in an area, and below their ability to sustain the deficit without damage, disruption or excessive costs'. If a rainfall deficiency occurs in the winter half-year, reservoirs, lakes and aquifers normally replenished at that season may fail to refill, and surface and ground water reserves may be inadequate during the following summer half-year, and the drought may be termed a hydrological drought. A drought during the growing season, when the loss of water to the atmosphere is normally greater than the total rainfall anyway, may be termed an agricultural drought. Every crop has its own drought-sensitive periods but since grass is the single most extensive crop Tabony uses grassland drought as a measure of agricultural stress in the country.

Incidence of the hazard

In *British rainfall* 1887 the following definitions of absolute and partial droughts were introduced:

Absolute drought is a period of at least 15 consecutive days to none of which is credited 0·25 mm of rain or more.
Partial drought is a period of at least 29 consecutive days, the mean daily rainfall of which does not exceed 0·25 mm.

Using these criteria Glasspoole and Rowsell (1947) have confirmed that there is a marked regional variation in the incidence of rainfall deficiency. Figure 5.1 shows that the average number of absolute droughts recorded in the years 1906–40 decreased from more than one per year in southern England, to less than one in every five years in northern Scotland. In addition while the longest recorded rainless spells over most of Scotland, northern England, Ireland and upland Wales hardly ever reach 30 days, this drought duration has been doubled in southern England where the longest rain-free period lasted more than 70 days in the spring of 1893 in the South East.

Sustained periods of below average rainfall are likely to have the maximum impact on water resources and on agricultural production and hence it is important to detail dry periods by duration. Table 5.1 lists the 10 driest spells over England and Wales since 1820 for various periods from 3 to 24 months. The 1975–6 drought is shown to be unprecedented for periods of 12, 16 and 18 months, but drier 3 and 24 months have been recorded. The table suggests that the drought represented an intensification of a rainfall deficit that had been a feature of the early 1970s. Two separate and non-overlapping 24-month periods; one beginning in July 1972 and the other in September 1974 are shown in the table. The 1975–6 dry period was not typical of some previous one-year droughts this century which persisted into late autumn and early winter. The most severe of these were from February to November 1921 (10 months), April 1933 to September 1934 (18 months) and February to November 1964 (10 months). In terms of duration and month of termination the 1975–6 drought is

Table 5.1 England and Wales rainfall: 10 driest periods of duration from 3 to 24 months since 1820 (starting date and rainfall totals given).

	3 months		mm	6 months		mm	12 months		mm
1	1938	Feb.	56	1921	Feb.	179	1975	Sept.	570
2	1929	Feb.	71	1976	Mar.	204	1854	Feb.	618
3	1893	Mar.	71	1887	Feb.	221	1920	Nov.	618
4	1868	May	74	1929	Jan.	230	1887	Feb.	624
5	1854	Feb.	74	1870	Apr.	241	1963	Dec.	637
6	1976	June	76	1826	Mar.	249	1933	Apr.	651
7	1844	Apr.	77	1893	Mar.	256	1857	Dec.	661
8	1947	Aug.	82	1959	Apr.	261	1904	Mar.	667
9	1963	Dec.	83	1896	Jan.	263	1955	July	670
10	1921	May	88	1939	Feb.	264	1863	Nov.	673

	16 months		mm	18 months		mm	24 months		mm
1	1975	May	756	1975	Mar.	908	1853	Oct.	1439
2	1854	Feb.	811	1853	Dec.	933	1932	Nov.	1439
3	1933	Apr.	855	1887	Jan.	997	1862	Nov.	1461
4	1887	Feb.	857	1933	Apr.	1003	1887	Feb.	1493
5	1920	Aug.	880	1873	Feb.	1031	1974	Sept.	1496
6	1873	Apr.	899	1857	Dec.	1032	1972	July	1497
7	1857	Nov.	907	1863	Feb.	1043	1904	Oct.	1507
8	1943	Feb.	909	1943	Feb.	1044	1857	Feb.	1512
9	1963	Dec.	920	1963	Dec.	1047	1920	Aug.	1513
10	1869	June	928	1921	Jan.	1061	1947	Aug.	1520

Table 5.2 Frequency of occurrence of specified dry periods in England and Wales, starting in a given month (per cent of 1916–50 average rainfall).

Frequency of occurrence (1 in x years)	Duration of dry period (months)									
	1	3	6	9	12	16	18	24	30	36
5	63·1	78·3	84·4	87·2	88·9	90·3	90·8	92·0	92·8	93·4
10	46·6	67·9	76·8	80·9	83·3	85·4	86·2	88·0	89·2	90·1
20	**33·6**	59·6	70·7	75·7	78·8	81·5	82·5	**84·7**	86·2	**87·4**
50	20·8	50·5	63·9	70·0	73·8	77·1	78·3	81·0	**82·9**	84·3
100	14·2	44·6	59·5	66·3	70·5	74·2	75·5	78·6	80·7	82·3
200	9·6	**39·3**	**55·4**	62·9	67·5	71·6	73·1	76·4	78·8	80·5
500	5·6	33·0	50·7	58·9	**63·9**	68·4	**70·1**	73·8	76·4	78·3
1000	3·7	28·9	47·4	**56·1**	61·4	**66·2**	68·0	71·9	74·7	76·7

comparable with that of 1933–4, when large areas of central England received below 70% of average rainfall.

The spatial extent of drought is largely masked by the areal average figures given in Table 5.1. During the driest calendar months on record (e.g. June 1925) no measurable rain has been noted over more than 6000 sq. km. Figure 5.2 shows the spatial distribution of the rainfall pattern over the UK for the 16 months May 1975 to August 1976, and it can be seen that rainfall was less than

60% of average over a wide area from southern England to Yorkshire, and only in extreme northwest Scotland was precipitation normal. It is not possible to find a rainfall deficit of similar magnitude and duration in records going back to 1727. Qualitative records from mediaeval written sources suggest it is possible that the drought of 1975–6 could have been the worst since 1252–3.

Because the drought of 1975–6 was unique in the context of available rainfall records, it is difficult to use statistical analysis to determine the likelihood of

Figure 5.2   Spatial distribution of rainfall May 1975–August 1976 as percentage of 1916–50 mean.

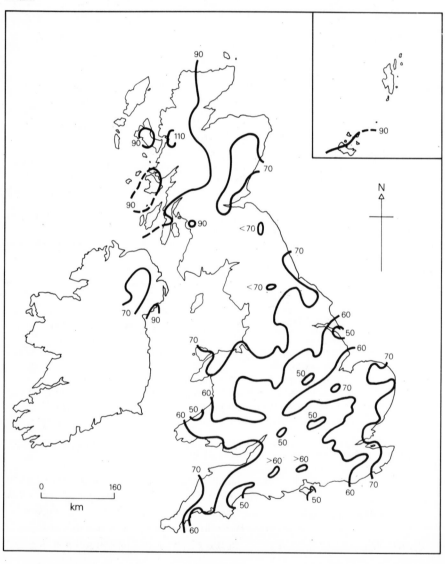

future recurrences. Frequences as rare as this, which are orders of magnitude greater than the length of the record cannot be defined with any precision. However, the Meteorological Office has developed a method to estimate the frequency of occurrence of specific lengths of any dry period from one to 36 months duration in England and Wales (Wright 1976). It needs to be stressed that in Table 5.2 return periods corresponding to given rainfall percentages may only be accurate within a range of between a half and twice the return period. Taking these reservations into account it seems possible that the 9 and 16 month periods starting in December and May 1975 respectively could have a return period of about 1000 years. The distribution of the return period of the 16 month

Figure 5.3 Return period of 1975–6 rainfall with a random start. The lines join areas with a probability of a 16 month period of only 64% of the long term average rainfall.

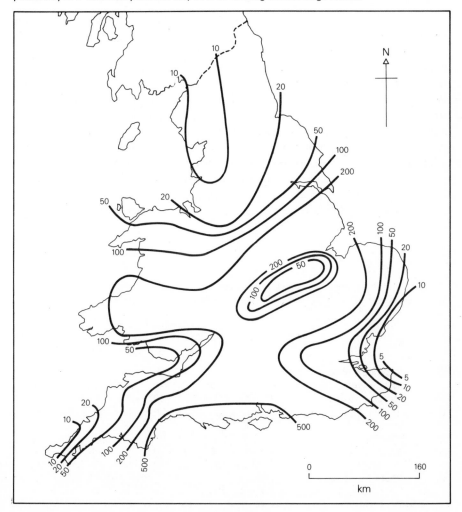

dry period of 1975–6 for a random start is shown in Figure 5.3. It is clear that conditions were not unusual for a 16-month dry period starting in any month in the North of England, in the extreme southwest and along the east coast. Along the south coast from Dorset to Sussex a return period of 1 in 500 years is indicated (Gibb & Richards 1978). Of course long-term changes in our climate, such as have occurred in the past, may well influence the frequency of drought, and it may be unwise to assume that the generally moist period with reliable rainfall which characterised the first half of this century will persist into the future (Lamb 1977). However, although variability of rainfall about the mean from epoch to epoch is to be expected there is no clear evidence that it has significantly increased. The relatively dry weather experienced in the 1970s does not necessarily suggest that abnormal departures from the historic pattern of average annual rainfall are to be expected more frequently in future in the British Isles.

While in terms of rainfall the 16-month period May 1975 to August 1976 was the driest such period since records began, for river flows the drought had a wide range of return periods which were often markedly different even at the same gauging station for different durations (Hamlin & Wright 1978). The mechanisms that give rise to low flows include catchment characteristics such as soil type, geology and topography, as well as the level of precipitation. The most important use of many rivers at least during periods of low flows, is for water supply, so that the return period of lowflow events (Table 5.3) at a selection of river gauge stations is both a measure of hydrological drought and a tool for the adequate management of water supplies during future drought periods.

The immediate cause of drought in the British Isles is the dislocation of the normal atmospheric circulation and its replacement by persistent anticyclonic systems over the Atlantic–European sector of the northern hemisphere. These anticyclones may be of two kinds:

Table 5.3 Return period (years) of low flow events 1975–6 (after Hamlin & Wright 1978).

Years of record	River gauge	Duration (months)								
		1	2	3	4	5	6	9	16	18
63	Yorkshire Bridge, R. Derwent	25	40	25	15	9	10	7	25	15
44	Bedford, Gt. Ouse	50	35	20	20	20	20	20	20	20
94	Teddington, R. Thames	90	70	50	35	30	30	35	30	30
18	Allbrook, R. Itchen	40	40	50	50	30	70	50	20	15
56	Bewdley, R. Severn	200	200	200	100	60	35	7	45	30
69	Caban Coch, Elan	100	200	100	100	70	70	8	40	40
20	Chain Bridge, R. Usk	50	200	100	100	60	30	15	30	25
50	Stocks Reservoir, R. Hodder, Lancs.	10	20	100	10	7	9	4	5	9

(a) North-eastward extensions of the semi-permanent Azores high across southern England. Frequently northern Scotland remains under the influence of travelling depressions and has normal or even above normal rainfall.

(b) Persistent or repetitive blocking anticyclones centred near to or over Britain. The normal westerly flow, with its travelling depressions is diverted north, and sometimes also south of the high pressure cell. On occasions such a circulation pattern can persist for periods of weeks, often breaking down for a short time only to re-establish itself again.

Figure 5.4 shows that during the 1975–6 drought surface pressure was above normal over the British Isles in association with the recurrent blocking that took place. The positive anomaly of 5 mb over the British Isles is greater than three standard deviations from the mean and represents an occurrence with an expectation of something less than 1 in 500. However, although these anomalies had dramatic consequences for the British Isles they were probably the result of only rather minor fluctuations or readjustments in the large scale atmospheric circulation which caused compensating changes elsewhere.

Undoubtedly the maintenance of a drought-type circulation for 16 months was the result of the complicated interaction between a number of large scale meteorological and oceanographic factors, and Ratcliffe (1977) has presented a comprehensive analysis of these. Among the most important interrelated features would seem to be:

(a) The run of mild winters in the early 1970s over Europe led to a shift in the position of the area of polar coldness to Canada and an intensification of the mid-latitude westerly flow over the North Pacific. Enhanced Pacific flow has been noted as stimulating blocking circulations over Europe on other occasions.

(b) Sea surface temperature anomaly patterns over the North Atlantic favoured the maintenance of blocking by steering depressions north-eastwards towards Iceland and Greenland (Perry 1976).

(c) The characteristics of the surface in the region of the British Isles increased the stability of the anticyclonic regime. Excessive dryness of the ground, especially in early summer 1976 with high value of net radiational heating of the ground led to a lack of available moisture over Europe, and numerical experiments suggest this factor may be of relevance to the prolongation of the drought.

If indeed climatic anomalies developing before the onset of the drought were important this implies a limited forecasting ability (Kelly & Wright 1978). Numerical modelling of climatic change processes may help in the future to define cause and effect in the many interactive components of the ocean–atmosphere system, but meanwhile work on the causes of drought highlights the need for continual monitoring of all aspects of the climate system.

Figure 5.4 Surface pressure anomalies during the 1975–6 drought and the position of the mid-latitude jet stream.

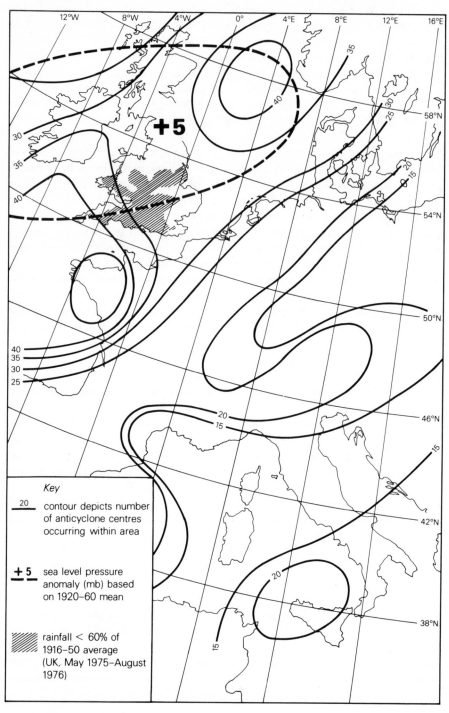

Key

20 ____ contour depicts number of anticyclone centres occurring within area

+5 sea level pressure anomaly (mb) based on 1920–60 mean

▨▨ rainfall < 60% of 1916–50 average (UK, May 1975–August 1976)

Costs and effects of the hazard

The responses of different water sources – rivers, ground water, and reservoirs to a drought are quite different and not surprisingly the response to drought differs over the country. Droughts cannot be prevented from occurring and the major protection against them involves the storage of water either underground in groundwater reserves or in surface reservoirs. Ground water provides about one-quarter of the total volume of water used in England and Wales and aquifers are particularly dependent upon winter rainfall for recharge, so that a series of dry winters will result in depletion of groundwater storage. Compared with surface supplies, groundwater reserves show a delayed response to rainfall deficiency and even during the 1975–6 drought although the water level in boreholes and wells fell to unprecedented levels, abstraction was able to continue. Surface reservoirs also tend to fill during the winter months and in a very dry year to become progressively depleted through the summer and autumn. The design of a system of water storage to utilise available rainfall involves both considerations of the volume needed to meet estimated demands to a specified degree of reliability and an analysis of the hydrological characteristics of the catchment. To expand surface water storage normally requires major engineering work, and is thus costly and can only be considered a long-term measure of drought control.

Water resources in England and Wales are already highly developed, but the demand for water continues to grow by about 2% per year. England and Wales have significantly smaller resources of water in relation to their population than any other country in Europe. In regions such as South Wales and South West England with a high proportion of older smaller reservoirs, the effects of the 1975–6 drought were particularly severe, with reservoir levels critically low and with little flexibility available to utilise other water resources (Booker & Mildren 1977). Over half a million people in southeast Wales experienced rota cuts for periods of between 7 and 11 weeks between July and September 1976, and these lasted for up to 17 hours a day while in Devon between 65 and 70 000 people out of a population of over 800 000 were placed on standpipe rationing for between one and three weeks. The severe water shortage of 1975–6 highlighted the constraints under which the Water Authorities had to operate to counter the effects of drought. Existing legislation (principally the Water Act 1958) allowing restrictions on the use of water (e.g. the banning of the use of hosepipes) had to be augmented by new legislation and the Drought Act (1976) became law on 6 August 1976. As part of the government's emergency programme a Drought Minister was appointed later in August and the Department of the Environment opened an emergency centre to co-ordinate response to the drought hazard. Short-term emergency measures included the laying of temporary water-pipelines, the use of tankers to carry emergency supplies and an intensive water saving publicity campaign. Business, industry and private consumers co-operated in making voluntary water savings and in the worse affected areas these savings reached 25% of normal consumption. Some industries had pre-pared contingency plans on the strength of early warnings in the spring of 1976 by the Confederation of British Industry to its members. There were three main impacts of the drought on industry:

(a) On production processes – water shortages stimulated recycling of sup-plies. In the most critically affected areas some reorganisation of industrial processes was necessary. The threat of large scale shut-down, shortened working weeks and unemployment appeared in August 1976, but fortu-nately the arrival of copious rainfall during the autumn averted these threats.

(b) On factory domestic services and operations – canteens economised, British Rail stopped washing trains and vehicle washing plants were closed.

(c) On the availability of some sections of the work force due to domestic restrictions at home – female employees, for example had to respond to curtailed school hours necessitated by water restrictions.

In South West England the most severe phase of the drought in the summer of 1976 coincided with the peak holiday season, and the influx of visitors increased the demand for water in the region.

The cost of the drought to the Water Authorities was considerable with the South-West Water Authority running up a bill of over £1 million as a result of the cost of stand-pipes, the massive publicity campaign and the need to install extra pumping equipment and temporary pipelines. The drought was a consider-able test for the ten newly created Regional Water Authorities (see Fig. 5.5) formed by the Water Act 1973. This legislation had increased the size of the local water supply and planning bodies, and one advantage of the larger units was that water could more readily be transferred to mitigate the effect of the drought in those areas most critically affected. Not surprisingly the 1975–6 drought led to further considerations of the case for a national water network, but it needs to be remembered that public water supplies in England and Wales take only about 8% of the runoff from rainfall in an average year and this figure is expected to reach only 11% by 2001. It seems likely that the response to future droughts will depend on how much people are prepared to pay for their water supplies. The experience of summer 1976 suggests that in extreme situations some consumers might be willing to pay for expensive temporary solutions such as using road tankers to carry water or even shipping water from abroad.

Not only problems of water supply, but also difficulties with water quality can arise in a drought. Many activities within the hydrological cycle can be affected directly or indirectly by drought conditions including treatment of sewage and eutrophication processes in rivers and reservoirs. Saline incursions occurred in the lower reaches of many East Anglian rivers in 1976 as river flows diminished and some cattle were affected by saline poisoning. Fish mortality rates increased as a result of exceptional conditions in natural watercourses. The most notable change in the quality of river water occurred in the post-drought period in the autumn of 1976 when there was a rapid increase in the concentration of nitrates (see p. 136) which led to restrictions in the quantities of water abstracted from rivers for public water supply.

The effect of drought on British agriculture can be considerable and the cost to the nation in lost crops of the 1975–6 drought was estimated at over £500 millions. A soil moisture deficit (SMD) develops when extraction of water from the soil by evaporation or transpiration is not compensated by rainfall or irrigation. SMD is defined as the amount of rainfall needed to bring the soil to 'field capacity'. This refers to the moisture content of the soil when it is holding all the water it can against the force of gravity. Grass growth is noticeably affected when SMD exceeds 50 mm and by August 1976 SMD was greater than

Figure 5.5   The regional water authorities in the UK.

125 mm over most of England and Wales, and reached 100 mm in southeast Ireland. Short-rooted vegetation became dessicated and animals had to be fed expensive hay and concentrates, while milk yields fell and lambs took longer to fatten. Large farming organisations dispatched whole herds of cattle to areas less severely affected by the drought. Root crops were badly affected and fresh vegetable prices reached very high levels. Farm incomes in the UK in 1976 fell 9% in real terms. Some cases of poisoning resulted from stock foraging for food where pastures were bare. Longer-term effects of the drought included an enhanced persistence of soil-acting herbicides and residues, and a build up of certain pests and diseases favoured by the weather. Cox (1978) has provided a

Figure 5.6   Frequency of irrigation need over England and Wales expressed as number of years out of ten.

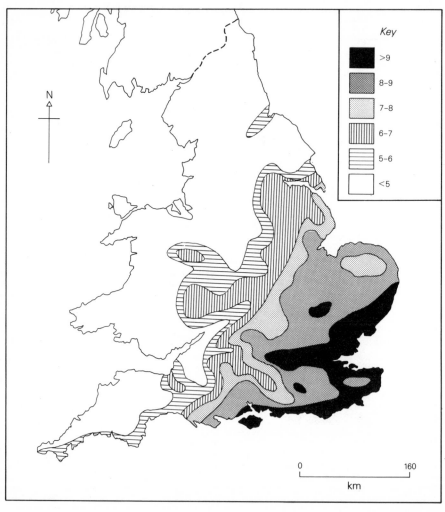

useful guide to the effects of the drought on farming and country life. Agricultural drought is sufficiently common in the British Isles for farmers to have
adopted irrigation as a form of climatic control. Natural rainfall is supplemented
by irrigation to increase and guarantee yields from crops. The extent of irrigation practice is determined by the new economic return resulting from the
improved yields obtained. The greatest demand for irrigation is in the drier
south-eastern parts of England, and it can be seen from Figure 5.6 that southeast
of a line from Hull to Torquay irrigation is beneficially applied in one year out of
two, while in the south-eastern coastal areas some irrigation is desirable every
summer. Crops with short growing seasons, such as salad produce, can benefit
from irrigation for short periods of the growth cycle, while a crop such as grass
may require irrigation at various times between April and September. In
planning the day to day practice of irrigation meteorological help is available to
farmers based on rainfall and soil-moisture deficit data. The most common
source of water for irrigation purposes is from surface streams, although the
potential demand in the South East can exceed the dry weather flow of rivers in
the area. It has been estimated that about 607 000 hectares could benefit from
irrigation in an average summer, although at present only about half this area is
actually treated.

During drought periods woods and heathland are susceptible to fire damage
often caused by carelessly thrown matches or by sunlight focused through
broken glass. During the summer of 1976 serious damage occurred on common-
land and heathland especially in Wales and southern England. Firemen, troops
and civilian volunteers worked long hours to keep fire outbreaks under control,
but thousands of acres of valuable trees and plantations were destroyed. In
Devon alone, the fire loss was over £1 million. The losses of flora and fauna were
considerable, and much concern was voiced concerning the survival of the rarest
of our breeding birds, especially the Dartford Warbler, that nests on the Dorset
heaths. Huge numbers of trees were killed as a direct result of the drought,
especially those on the shallower soils. In the New Forest alone 8000 mature
beeches and sycamores were estimated to have died. An oak tree requires about
150 gallons of water a day. The shortage of water robbed older trees of the
strength necessary to combat disease and the spread of Dutch elm disease (see p.
177) was intensified.

Damage to buildings by subsidence-related damage has been regarded as
presenting only a slight risk except in such obvious hazard zones as those
involving mining subsidence or landslipping. As a result of the 1975–6 drought,
movement of the foundations of thousands of houses took place especially those
built on shrinkable clay, and the result was widespread structural damage. The
problem was most widespread in the south of England where these clays
predominate. The British Insurance Association estimated that between £50–60
millions was paid out for subsidence claims in 1976, representing over 20 000
claims. Insurance cover against this hazard commenced in 1971 although major
damage to building foundations had occurred in other droughts, notably in
1947. Many affected householders remained uninsured, often because of

ignorance of the new cover available. In the worst affected areas in 1976, more than 100 dwellings in 100 000 were subject to subsidence claims. The repair of buildings is expensive and underpinning often involves substantial capital expenditure. When subsidence becomes widespread on an estate of houses the problem can receive wide publicity and lead to a diminution in market values, irrespective of any damage to a particular house or flat. Widespread and continuing claims have ensured that one legacy of the drought has been increased insurance premiums. As M. J. Clark points out (in Gregory & Doornkamp 1980) 'it is clear that property damage triggered or exacerbated by the drought was one of the most significant tangible impacts of the 1976 event'.

One of the outstanding features of the weather over the British Isles during the remarkable summer of 1976, was a prolonged heat wave which lasted for more than 2 weeks and was probably unparalleled for 250 years. The high temperatures increased the effects of the drought on plants and crops. In addition, weekly death registrations in Greater London increased. Mortality rates of old people, especially those suffering from cardiovascular and respiratory complaints rose markedly (Macfarlane & Waller 1976). Recent analysis of daily mortality data shows that increases in mortality also occur during less severe hot spells (Macfarlane 1978). Research suggests that the heat acts as a catalyst bringing forward the date of deaths of older people already seriously ill. By contrast baby deaths in England and Wales in 1976 fell and the Office of Population Census attributed this to the fine weather of the summer following upon a mild winter.

Conclusions

The 1975–6 drought represents a natural hazard with a long return period which had a considerable impact on social and economic life as well as upon the physical environment. In general, farmers and growers had the rainfall deficit brought to their attention far earlier than people in towns, but by the closing weeks of the drought the magnitude and severity of the event and the ways in which the mass media portrayed and communicated information about it, ensured that its effects came to the notice of most people in England and Wales. The greatest drought for perhaps 1000 years revealed not only how vulnerable our crowded and complicated civilisation is, but also how profligate has been our use of water resources. Because rainfall in the British Isles is normally at least adequate there has been no dramatic evidence of need for a national drought-alleviation or drought-control programme. A key lesson learnt by the water supply industry (National Water Council 1977) is the need for flexible and adaptable deployment of existing resources, rather than the preparation of detailed contingency plans for any future eventuality. Since no precedent existed the response to the hazard was an inchoate policy concentrating on drought relief and emergency provision. Fortunately the period of water stress ended more rapidly than had been thought likely, as the autumn of 1976 brought heavy rainfall, and in retrospect the policies developed and the legislation introduced in general proved adequate. With the advantage of hindsight it can be suggested that the real impact of the drought may have been more complex but less damaging than was perceived at the time. The final evaluation is by no means negative, many activities adapted well to the stress experienced, and in other cases rapid adjustments were made in response to this and the possibility of similar future hazard events.

Bibliography

Booker, F. and J. Mildren 1977. *The drought in the SW*. Univ. of Exeter Industrial Arch. Group. Callington, Cornwall: Penwell Ltd.

Cox, E. 1978. *The great drought of 1976*. London: Hutchinson.

Gibb, O. and H. J. Richards 1978. Planning for development of groundwater and surface water resources. *Proc. R. Soc. Lond. A.* **363**, 109–30.

Glasspoole, J. and H. Rowsell 1947. Absolute droughts and partial droughts over the Br. Isles 1906–40. *Meteorol. Mag.* **76**, 201–5.

Gregory, K. J. and J. C. Doornkamp 1980. *Atlas of the drought*. London: Institute of British Geographers.

Hamlin, M. J. and C. E. Wright 1978. The effects of drought on the river systems. *Proc. R. Soc. Lond. A.* **363**, 69–96.

Kelly, P. M. and P. B. Wright 1978. The European drought of 1975–6 and its climatic context. *Progr. Phys. Geog.* **2**, 237–63.

Lamb, H. H. 1977. *Climate past, present and future*. vol. 2. London: Methuen.

Macfarlane, A. 1978. Daily mortality and environment in English conurbations: deaths during summer hot spells in Greater London. *Environ. Res.* **15**, 332–41.

Macfarlane, A. and R. E. Waller 1976. Short-term increases in mortality during heat-waves. *Nature* **264**, 434–6.

Meaden, G. T. 1976. North-west Europe's great drought. *J. Meteorol.* **1**, 379–83.

Ministry of Agriculture and Fisheries 1954. *The calculations of irrigation need*. Tech. Bull., no. 4. London: HMSO.

Mortimore, K. O. 1976. The great drought of 1975–6. *J. Meteorol.* **1**, 373–8.

Murray, R. 1977. The 1975–6 drought over the UK – hydrometeorological aspects. *Meteorol. Mag.* **106**, 129–45.

National Water Council 1977. *The 1975–6 drought*. London: NWC.

Perry, A. H. 1976. The long drought of 1975–6. *Weather* **31**, 328–34.

Ratcliffe, R. A. S. 1977. A synoptic climatologist's view of the 1975–6 drought. *Meteorol. Mag.* **106**, 145–54.

Tabony, R. C. 1977. Drought classification and a study of drought at Kew. *Meteorol. Mag.* **106**, 1–10.

Wright, C. E. 1976. Once in 1000 years? *Water* **11**, 1–6.

6 *Fog*

'The British are a people who enshrine a disagreeable combination of
cloud, mist and fog amongst their national glories.'
John Osborne 1968

Years ago large towns were notorious for their severe dense fogs known in
London as 'pea-soupers'. Now however, as a result of legislation and the spread
of smokeless zones (see p. 133) fogs are not as dirty as they once were, but remain
a hazard particularly because of their effects on transportation. While fog is often
associated with man-made pollution this is not always so. In Nottingham for
example, it has been found that the number of fogs is proportional to smoke
concentration only when concentration exceeds a threshold of pollution. Con-
versely atmospheric pollution is not always associated with fog. This is the
justification for considering fog and atmospheric pollution separately in different
chapters, although obviously it needs to be remembered that there are links
between the two.

With the advent of motorways and our ever-growing dependence on air
transport, disruptions caused by fog have become increasingly costly in terms of
lives, time and money. Organisations concerned with minimising the operational problems caused by fog need to be informed of the physical nature of the
fog in order that realistic assessments of the feasibilities of proposed practical
solutions can be assessed.

Incidence of the hazard

Fog is defined as occurring when visibility is less than 1000 m irrespective of
whether the obscurity is produced by water droplets or solid particles. Fog is
likely to be most hazardous when it is thick, and this adjective is used by
meteorologists when visibility is less than 200 m. The term 'dense fog' is used
when visibility is less than 50 m. The nature of fogs vary according to temperature, and two types that are common in the British Isles are:

(a)   Warm fog – which consists of a cloud of droplets which have a temperature
      above 0°C.
(b)   Supercooled fog – (sometimes referred to as freezing fog) – the droplets are
      in equilibrium with the atmosphere at a temperature which is equal to, or
      less than 0°C.

The occurrence of fog is associated with meteorological conditions which are
conducive to the cooling of air below its dew point. As Table 6.1 shows this may

Table 6.1 Summary of fog characteristics in Britain.

Type of fog	Season	Areas affected	Mode of formation	Mode of dispersal
radiation fog	October to March	inland areas, especially low lying, moist ground	cooling due to radiation from the ground on clear nights when the wind is light	dispersed by the sun's radiation or by increased wind
advection fog (a) over land	winter or spring	often widespread inland	cooling of warm air by passage over cold ground	dispersed by a change in air mass or by gradual warming of the ground
(b) over sea and coastline	spring and early summer	sea and coasts, may penetrate a few miles	cooling of warm air by passage over cold sea	dispersed by a change in air mass and may be cleared on coast by the sun's heating
frontal fog	all seasons	high ground	lowering of the cloud base along the line of the front	dispersed as the front moves and brings a change of air mass
smoke fog (smog)	winter	near industrial areas and large conurbations	similar to radiation fog	dispersed by wind increase or by convection

be achieved in a number of ways and a variety of different types of fog affect the British Isles. Radiation fog and smoke fog most commonly occur during anticyclonic spells and col situations when winds are light, while advection fog over coasts is usually associated with moist south-westerly airstreams. Advection fog inland may occur in winter when mild air is advected across a cold, snow-covered land surface. It is usually of quite a short duration since the warmer airstream soon raises the temperature of the ground. The most serious and persistent fogs inland are of the radiation type. Visibility tends to be least around and just after dawn, at the time of minimum temperature. On clear nights intense radiation cooling frequently produces low-level inversions of temperature. The temperature of the air increases with height up to 100–200 m above the ground, instead of decreasing as usual, and under such conditions the lower atmosphere will be extremely stable so that any pollution emitted will not easily be dispersed. Fog occurrence is affected by topography and large variations in visibility over short distances are quite common. Radiation fog in particular, is often a localised phenomenon and tends to be erratic in development and localised in extent. In sheltered valleys where the topography inhibits air movement and allows cold foggy air to 'pond up', fog frequencies will be highest. However, there is not always a simple relation between topography and fog. Eyre (1962) studied fog frequency in one winter in parts of Yorkshire using a dense network of observers, and the occasions with visibility less than 90 m are shown in Figure 6.1. The presence of towns, topography and probably other factors are of significance in determining the observed distribution. The

Figure 6.1   Occasions with visibility below 90 metres in Yorkshire in an average year.

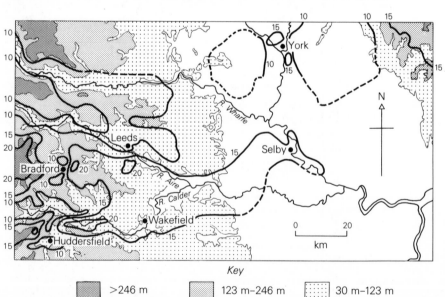

Key

> 246 m   123 m–246 m   30 m–123 m

increase in the number of fogs at high levels is due to the frequent descent of the cloud base to cover the hills.

Some idea of the general distribution of thick fogs is given by Figure 6.2. The most frequently affected areas lie in a zone from South East England across the Midlands to south Lancashire and west Yorkshire and northwards into North East England. High fog frequencies are shown in Figure 6.2 at some exposed coastal stations, such as Cape Wrath in northwest Scotland and these represent occasions of advection-type fogs. Winter fog was shown by Smith (1967) to be nearly twice as frequent at the inland stations. It needs to be stressed that radiation fog is often very patchy and may easily develop between the meteorological station network, and consequently may occur without being detected and noted in the meteorological statistics. Many meteorological stations are at airports which themselves tend to be located outside fog-prone areas. It follows that the statistics may give an unrepresentative or biased picture of the fog situation in a region. The relative lack of fog in summer is exaggerated because at that season 09.00 hours, the time of observation, is so long after sunrise that radiation fog formed overnight has often dispersed by then. About 90% of all observations of thick fog are made between September and March.

Widespread thick fog lasting a whole day is quite rare. Typically fog lasts only a few hours during the early part of the day, although it may reform again quite quickly after sunset. Studies in the London area suggest a continuous spell of 12 hours or more of fog with visibility less than 200 m can be expected about three times a year at Heathrow Airport, and once a year in central London. During the December 1952 fog episode, in the London area at Kew observatory, visibility was less than 10 m from the evening of the 5th until 06.00 hours on the 8th, and in central London fog persisted for about 114 hours. The frequency of thick fogs in the densely built up central parts of cities is less than in the suburbs, because of the greater warmth and lower humidities of the city centres at night (Brazell 1964). Changes of fog frequencies over long periods have been noted. The influence of the Clean Air Act of 1956 (see p. 133) may well account for some of the decrease in thick fog frequency noted at Manchester, Finningley (Yorkshire), Heathrow and other inland stations including rural and semi-rural sites. Dinsdale (1968) showed that frequencies of fog at Kew declined rapidly from the early 1950s to become comparable with those at sites in unpolluted areas. The evidence suggests that the Clean Air Act which was primarily designed to improve air quality in towns has also produced measurable decreases in fog frequency in many rural areas too.

Costs and effects of the hazard

Fog is a hazard to transport by land, sea and air and costly adjustments such as automatic aids for aircraft and safety signalling for rail transport are needed. It is only in road transport that adjustment is still seriously deficient, and a series of crashes on motorways over the last few years, extensively reported in the mass

Figure 6.2   Distribution of thick fog over the UK.

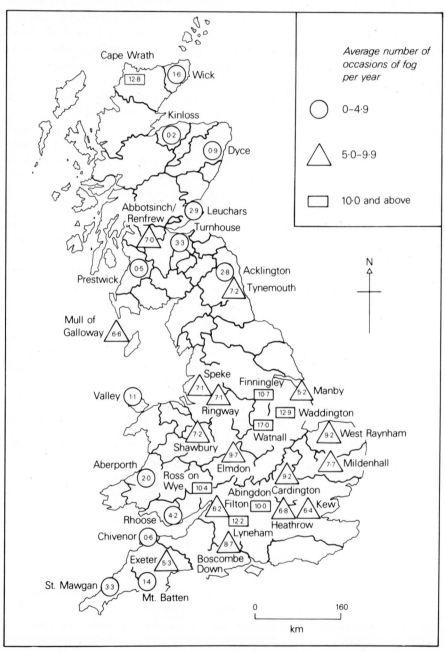

media, frequently under headlines such as 'motorway madness', have focused particular attention on this problem. It is unfortunate that the highest mean annual frequencies of thick fog are recorded in regions with the greatest density of motorways, and at a time when the roads are carrying an extremely large volume of commuter and commercial traffic. In fact from 1970–4 in the UK an average of only 4% of all total or serious injury accidents on the roads occurred in fog or mist. On motorways 6% of road casualties occurred in conditions of thick fog. Although the total number of accidents may be relatively small they are generally multiple collisions which often have severe human and economic repercussions. 60% of injury accidents in fog on motorways involved more than 2 vehicles compared with about 10% in clear weather. Traffic flow is disrupted and a large amount of material damage is caused. Thus in 1974 fog is estimated to have cost over £12 millions on the roads and a single accident can cost £½ million. This figure includes the costs of medical treatment, damage to vehicles and property, and administrative costs of police and insurance, but does not include the cost of delays to vehicles not directly involved. Two examples well illustrate this type of crash:

(a) In a multiple accident on the M6 in September 1971, 10 people were killed, 70 injured and more than 200 vehicles damaged.
(b) A fog accident between junctions 17 and 18 on the M1 on 13 March 1975, involved 204 vehicles over 20 km of carriageway and led to 6 deaths and 28 serious injuries.

The dates of these examples suggest that there are at least 7 months of the year when dense fog can occur during hours when the motorways are quite heavily used. Examination of the site of multiple motorway fog crashes (Fig. 6.3) reveals that most have occurred where the road crosses a valley or low-lying region. Eye-witness reports have often commented on the patchy nature of fog, so that fast moving vehicles may pass quickly from sunshine into a wall of fog, brake, and be run into from behind by other vehicles. On 30 November 1971, on the M1 in Bedfordshire a light breeze lifted a belt of fog over neighbouring fields onto the motorway which at that time was clear of fog, and an accident that killed 9 people and affected 100 vehicles resulted.

Work by climatologists at the University of Manchester has focused on the development of a simple model for predicting local potential fog 'blackspots' along motorway routes. The model incorporates environmental factors considered to be important in producing local radiation fog and has been designed to identify those localities where fog frequency will tend to be greatest, and where visibilities within the fog will be lowest. The Fog Potential Index (I_p) is derived by an expression of the form:

$$I_p = f(d_w, t_p, s_p, e_p)$$

where d_w expresses the distance of the location from standing water (rivers, canals, lakes, ponds, gravel working etc.) and the spatial extent of that surface

Figure 6.3   Fog prone areas and the site of multiple motorway accidents.

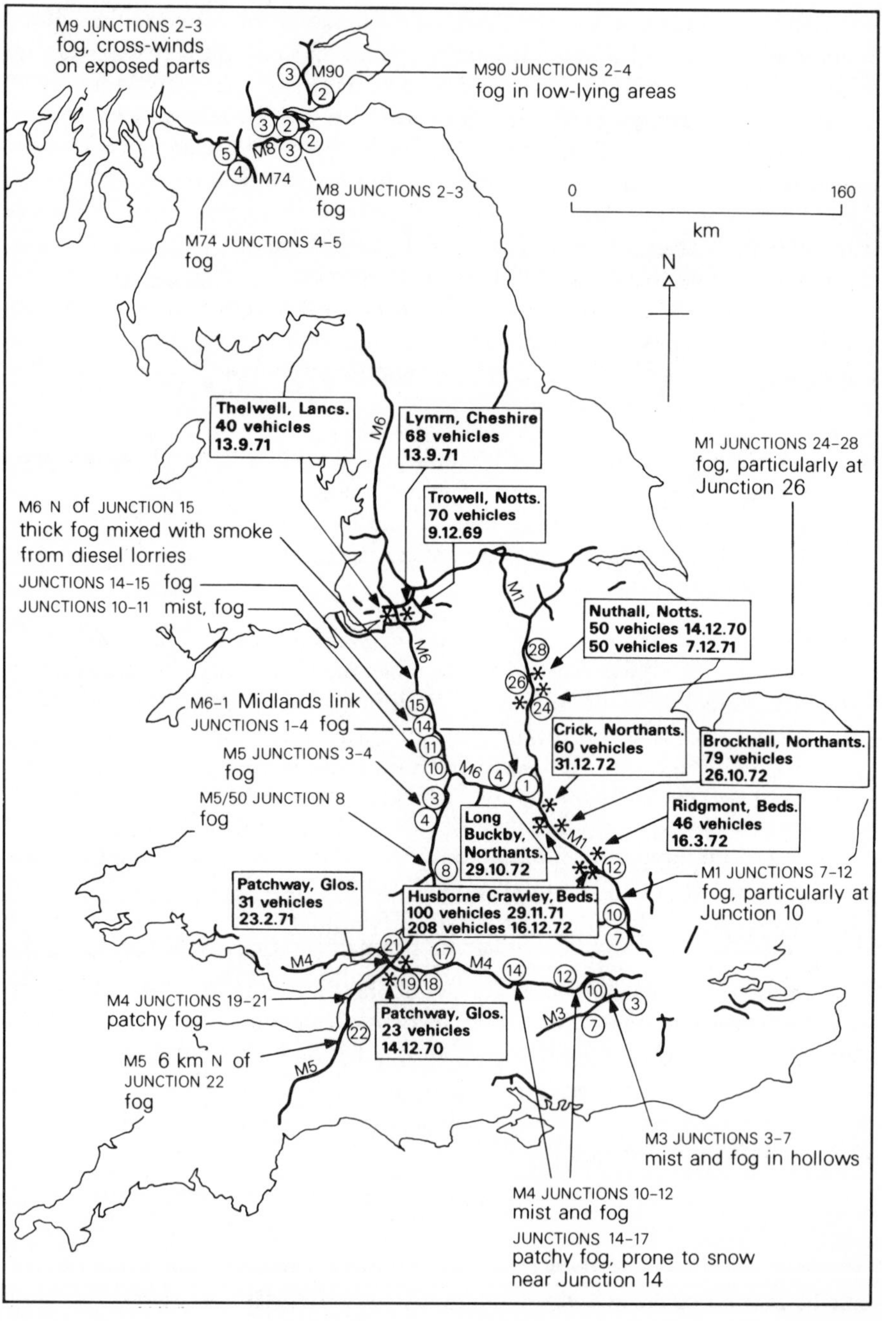

M9 JUNCTIONS 2–3
fog, cross-winds
on exposed parts

M90 JUNCTIONS 2–4
fog in low-lying areas

M8 JUNCTIONS 2–3
fog

M74 JUNCTIONS 4–5
fog

Thelwell, Lancs.
40 vehicles
13.9.71

Lymm, Cheshire
68 vehicles
13.9.71

Trowell, Notts.
70 vehicles
9.12.69

M6 N of JUNCTION 15
thick fog mixed with smoke
from diesel lorries

JUNCTIONS 14–15 fog

JUNCTIONS 10–11 mist, fog

M1 JUNCTIONS 24–28
fog, particularly at
Junction 26

Nuthall, Notts.
50 vehicles 14.12.70
50 vehicles 7.12.71

M6–1 Midlands link
JUNCTIONS 1–4 fog

M5 JUNCTIONS 3–4
fog

M5/50 JUNCTION 8
fog

Crick, Northants.
60 vehicles
31.12.72

Brockhall, Northants.
79 vehicles
26.10.72

Ridgmont, Beds.
46 vehicles
16.3.72

Long
Buckby,
Northants.
29.10.72

Patchway, Glos.
31 vehicles
23.2.71

Husborne Crawley, Beds.
100 vehicles 29.11.71
208 vehicles 16.12.72

M1 JUNCTIONS 7–12
fog, particularly at
Junction 10

M4 JUNCTIONS 19–21
patchy fog

Patchway, Glos.
23 vehicles
14.12.70

M5 6 km N of
JUNCTION 22
fog

M3 JUNCTIONS 3–7
mist and fog in hollows

M4 JUNCTIONS 10–12
mist and fog

JUNCTIONS 14–17
patchy fog, prone to snow
near Junction 14

0 _____ 160
km

N

water, t_p is a function of the local topography at the point p incorporating such factors as the form of the local topography (hill or valley, slope or plain), the size of the likely catchment for katabatic drainage towards point p, and whether the site is a recipient area for cold air flow or a donor (see p. 64), s_p is a function of the road topography at point p expressing the form of the road at that point (cutting or embankment) and orientation of the road which influences exposure. e_p incorporates a general expression for any environmental feature likely to help or hinder radiation fog formation, such as the proximity of woodland, urban areas, or pollution sources. The derived indices are comparative and designed to give the sort of information on a local scale that a road planner needs to make objective appraisals of alternative routes. The model is currently being tested in a study for a by-pass around a town in the East Midlands, over a large area of country in south Yorkshire for a proposed new road, and at two alternative crossing points of a river valley in the south of England. At particular fog blackspots, fog detectors, which allow continuous monitoring of visibility, are beginning to be used to augment observers' manual visibility readings. The Meteorological Office, the Road Research Laboratory and the Home Office have combined in a recent trial to evaluate potential low cost visibility instruments as possible aids in motorway traffic control.

Meteorologists have investigated a number of objective fog forecasting techniques, but visibility remains probably the most difficult of all meteorological phenomena to forecast accurately. Although several forecasting techniques appear to produce relatively good results at the airfields which recorded the observations on which they are based, problems arise when these forecasts are extended to cover a general area which exhibits wide geographical variations. One example chosen from many illustrates the importance of this point. At 08.00 hours on 12 January 1971 patches of fog were reported by an observer on the A1(M) in the West Riding. Six hours, and one multiple collision later, the Meteorological Office at Bawtry contacted the Motorway Police and advised them to issue a fog warning to motorists in the area.

The most obvious cause of horrific multiple accidents is that drivers are travelling too fast for prevailing weather conditions. Deprived of the normal visual aids for judging speed, and concerned that he may be hit from behind, a driver often seems unaware that he will be unable to brake without hitting the vehicle ahead in an emergency, and overdrives his visual range. Fog isolates the driver from his surrounding environment producing perceptual disorganisation. Awareness exists that fog is a hazard. A recent survey in the UK revealed that British drivers believe that fog is second only to drinking and driving in producing dangerous road situations. Remedial aids currently in use include fog warning systems operated from a control centre, speed restrictions, and convoys or platooning of vehicles (used successfully by West Yorkshire police, but very demanding of manpower and resources). In addition 140 km of low pressure sodium lighting at six fog-prone motorway locations chosen for their fog accident rates in the period 1969–71 are being installed as an experiment in improving visibility. Conventional high-level lighting can create a luminous glare in foggy conditions due to the scattering of light by the fog droplets. Research suggests that if lighting is to be used it should be low-level lighting directed at right angles to the drivers' line of sight. Research is continuing into the development of other countermeasures, including the provision of a simple in-vehicle radar system which could provide the driver with a warning if he is travelling too close behind the vehicle in front. Meanwhile extensive publicity campaigns designed to educate drivers and make them aware of the hazard continues. The Department of the Environment has issued a driving code for use in fog. The spread of local radio stations allows warning of local fog to be broadcast so that drivers with car radios can receive information on conditions occurring during their journey.

Fog was a major hazard to railway operations and Wintel (1960) claimed that an expenditure of £20 millions was necessary to increase safety by the extension of modern colour-light signalling and automatic warning systems to all main lines in Britain. Since that time the spending of large capital sums has helped to ensure that railway operations are less disrupted by fog than used to be the case. Only occasionally is it now necessary to introduce skeleton fog services. Despite increasingly sophisticated automatic landing equipment, poor visibility is a major impediment to airport operations, resulting in cancelled flights and loss of revenue for airlines and delay and extra expense for travellers. Artificial fog dispersal was used in Britain in World War II and consists of burning gasoline and evaporating airborne water droplets. The technique has proved to be too expensive for use commercially, although experiments have continued especially in France using jet engine exhaust heating. Fog halts flights in Britain's five major airports for over 1000 hours each year. Reduced visibility has been shown to be the most important causal factor in weather-related aircraft accidents (General Aviation Safety Committee 1979). Over the 10-year period 1967–76 there were 181 fatal accidents to UK registered powered aircraft of which over 29% were weather related. A study of the details of fatal accidents indicates that most of them were the result of the aircraft being flown into the ground or obstructions in conditions that precluded the pilot either from seeing the hazard in time to avoid it, or from controlling the aircraft by external visual means. Whether an aircraft can land in poor visibility depends upon the airfield's lighting system and the type of aircraft. A fully operational blind-landing system has been installed at Heathrow but there are only a few aircraft equipped to use it. The systems are too expensive for use at any but major airports.

Fog at sea is a serious hazard despite modern navigational aids. In the winter of 1971 a multiple collision involving a tanker and two freighters off Folkestone, led to the loss of 50 lives and £2½ millions worth of shipping. Between 1958 and 1971 80% of collisions in the Straits of Dover occurred during occasions when visibility was under 4 km.

Conclusions

Although the British Isles have been perceived as islands of frequent mist and fogs, and this feature of the climate has made a strong impression on visitors, the number of occasions of fog per year even in the most prone areas is only a tiny percentage of all days. Nevertheless the capricious nature of dense fog formation renders it an important potential hazard for the traveller. Many forms of public transport have adopted often costly adjustments to minimise disruption, but on the roads there remains a shortfall in our preparedness. Work continues on means of communicating warnings to drivers and other kinds of adjustments, but meanwhile it is often the case that the driver suffering damage to his vehicle is able to pass on most of his losses to others, who pay for accidents in the form of increased insurance premiums. Instrumental measurements of visibility using Visirange equipment, and transmissometers are being developed and can provide *in situ* data of reasonable accuracy. However, such instruments are costly and only a small number of sites can be monitored and planning permission is required for their installation.

Bibliography

Brazell, J. H. 1964. Frequency of dense and thick fog in central London as compared with frequency in outer London. *Meteorol. Mag.* **93**, 129–35.

Dinsdale, F. E. 1968. Fog frequencies at inland stations. *Meteorol. Mag.* **97**, 314–7.

Eyre, S. R. 1962. Fog in Yorkshire 1959–60. *Weather* **17**, 125–31.

General Aviation Safety Committee 1979. Aircraft accidents related to weather. *Weather* **34**, 269–74.

Smith, F. J. 1967. A comparison of the incidence of fog at a coastal station with that at an inland station. *Meteorol. Mag.* **96**, 77–81.

Wintel, B. J. 1960. Railways versus the weather. *Weather* **15**, 137–9.

SECTION B   OTHER TYPES OF
ENVIRONMENTAL HAZARDS

7 *Pollution hazards*

'This Smoke which is a Plague in so many other ways because it kills not at once but always since still to languish is worse than even Death itself.'

John Evelyn 1661

Introduction

Pollution can be defined as the release by Man of substances (or energy) to the environment in quantities which damage his resources. Pollution can be regarded as a form of resource misuse arising because individuals can transfer the costs of removing their waste products to others. Recently there has been an increased concern shown for environmental quality (Coppock & Wilson 1974) and a general recognition that pollution of all sorts impairs the quality of the environment. The effects of pollution can be dramatic, as in the case of severe air pollution episodes with their attendant rise in the death rate; or less obvious and more circumstantial, for example the higher death rates from certain diseases in areas of heavy metal contamination. In addition new technologies are constantly resulting in new pollutants.

Legislation to control pollution in the UK was first passed more than a century ago with the Alkali Act of 1863, setting up what is known today in England and Wales as HM Alkali and Clean Air Inspectorate. The standards of the emissions of many industries are set and enforced by the inspectors who operate on the basis of adopting the 'best practicable means' to minimise pollution. The Inspectorate co–operates with industry, preferring to apply persuasive pressure rather than to prosecute offending polluters. In deciding what is practicable the Inspector must take account of the present state of technical knowledge, the economics of the situation and the pollution already existing. The British tradition of voluntary compliance usually does not require the designation of precisely defined standards. In a study of national policies used to combat environmental problems Wall (1976) notes that the British approach assumes that pollution is bad and that anything which can be done to reduce pollution levels is good and is likely to result in net benefits to society.

The costs of pollution abatement to achieve a desired environmental quality objective vary from one location to another depending on the assimilative capacity of the local environment. To advise the government an independent Standing Royal Commission on Environmental Pollution was set up in 1970 to advise on matters concerning the pollution of the environment. The UK is probably one of the most intensively environment-monitored of industrial countries. The aim is to protect human life. Man is sustained by other species in his environment – crops, domestic animals and fish – and if there is a significant ecological disruption on a wide enough scale through pollution, Man himself cannot escape the hazard.

A principle embodied in pollution control legislation is that the polluter must pay for his pollution. Lord Ritchie-Calder has described pollution as 'a crime compounded of ignorance and avarice'. Only a few spatial studies of the pollution process in all media has been carried out in the UK (e.g. Wood *et al.* 1974). Rees (1977) has suggested 5 main methods of reducing environmental pollution:

(a) Pricing all environmental resources and thus charging producers and households for waste disposal. Goods produced by high-waste generating methods would increase in price and consumers would theoretically switch to products involving lower environmental costs. Most pollution is an unintentional by-product of the production of socially useful goods. In most cases we wish to limit the polluting activity only so long as we continue to gain more than we lose when all costs and benefits are considered (Charles & Button 1976).

(b) Establishing quality standards and ensuring that individual discharges are compatible with these standards. In Britain there is a more limited use of environmental standards than in the USA or in other EEC countries.

(c) Subsidising producers to reduce the level of waste discharged into the environment. This can be inefficient since the severity of environmental hazard caused by the same discharge varies from place to place.

(d) Banning and severely controlling discharges. Frequently used in the UK together with (b).

(e) Increasing the capacity of the environment to absorb waste, e.g. re-aerating streams.

It is convenient to classify pollutants according to the environment medium through which they are diffused; air, water and land, and such an approach has been adopted where possible in the remaining sections of this chapter. Pollutants like noise, or heavy metals are multi-media pollutants and are treated in separate sections.

Air pollution

The causes of air pollution episodes. Air pollution episodes may be defined as short-term periods of consecutive days during which the ground-level recorded concentrations reach exceptionally high levels, which can be both dangerous and economically costly to the community (Elsom 1979). Two conditions are required to produce an air pollution episode. The first is the emission of sufficient quantities of pollutants, and the second the necessary adverse meteorological conditions to cause the emitted pollutants to reach high ground-level concentrations. In Britain air pollution levels are invariably higher in winter than summer, and reach their peak levels when inversion conditions ensure that the natural cleansing properties of the atmosphere are most weakly developed. When the temperature decreases with height, as it normally does, good dispersion and vertical transport of pollutants can be expected. When the temperature increases with height in the first few kilometres of the atmosphere conditions are said to be stable, and such conditions prevent vertical dispersion, trapping pollutants close to the surface. Air pollution episodes develop under stable stagnating air masses, when there is an inversion of the normal temperature profile in the lower atmosphere. During winter anticyclonic conditions temperatures are often low at the ground as a result of night time radiation under clear skies, and the light wind or calm conditions lead to marked stability of the atmosphere which severely inhibits dispersal of pollutants, either horizontally or vertically. Pollution concentrations accumulate beneath the 'inversion lid' and if the solar radiation during the day fails to break up the inversion, the lowest levels of the atmosphere become increasingly charged with pollutants. Pollution levels may be particularly high in certain topographical situations, such as valleys and enclosed basins, which inhibit lateral drift of the air (Bach 1972). During high pollution episodes a positive feedback can maintain or even increase pollution levels, since the formation of smog reduces solar radiation reaching the ground which would otherwise create thermal overturnings to disperse the pollutants. Furthermore reduced solar radiation increases the need for the space-heating of homes and premises, so increasing the emission of pollutants.

The effects on health. The most dramatic manifestation of the harmful effect of pollution is the increased mortality and morbidity which accompany heavily polluted episodes. From 5–8 December 1952, London experienced one of the worst air pollution disasters ever reported, with at least 4000 excess deaths attributable to the 'smog'. Such mortality was as dramatic as in the cholera epidemics of the 19th century. Deaths were mostly among the elderly and the sick and were primarily due to respiratory or cardiovascular diseases. Deaths from bronchitis increased by a factor of 10, influenza by 7 and pneumonia by 5. Although appalling, the excess deaths need putting in perspective, and the Clean Air Society points out that in 1952 12 000 Londoners were destined to die in January and February 1953 from an influenza epidemic that was then on its way. Before the epidemic arrived 4000 chesty persons died one month earlier than their expected demise. Each lost one-tenth of a year of life, i.e. in all 400 years of life were lost, which was the same amount of years lost as that which occurs every week from motor vehicle accidents in the affected area. In addition during the 1952 episode there was an enormous increase in the number of acute but non–fatal respiratory illnesses.

It is believed that tiny particles, many of them acidic with irritant properties, can penetrate deeply into the tiny air sacks deep in the lung resulting in destruction of lung tissue. If destruction of blood vessels also occurs this results in extra strain being put on the heart which has to work harder to pump blood. Lawther (1973) has shown how variations in mortality occur with less dramatic changes in pollution levels in Greater London (Fig. 7.1). Air pollution episodes in London have been fairly common, and in December 1962 during a five-day period of smog conditions, there was actually higher sulphur dioxide (SO_2) levels than during the disaster 10 years earlier. On this occasion there were about 750 excess deaths. Wilkins (1954) has attempted to map the SO_2 pollution in the London area during the 1952 smog episode (Fig. 7.2). Two areas of maximum pollution occurred with the highest levels measured being recorded in the Westminster area. The concentration of SO_2 was very closely correlated with the increase in deaths during the smog period.

Laboratory tests have failed so far to identify the pollutants responsible for exacerbating existing diseases and this has made it more difficult to obtain direct cause–effect relationships between air pollution and morbidity. In particular it is difficult to demonstrate chronic effects caused by continued exposure to moderate levels of air pollution, but we know that bronchitis is a town disease in Britain, particularly common in the heavily industrialised and polluted areas, and between 15 and 20% of morbidity from bronchitis in the UK may be due to exposure to air pollution over a considerable number of years. In an area like Greater Manchester this is equivalent to between 400 and 650 deaths per annum. Inhalation of urban air has often been blamed for the development of lung cancer, although it is now known that tobacco and particularly cigarette smoking is the major cause of this disease.

Figure 7.1 Mortality and pollution.

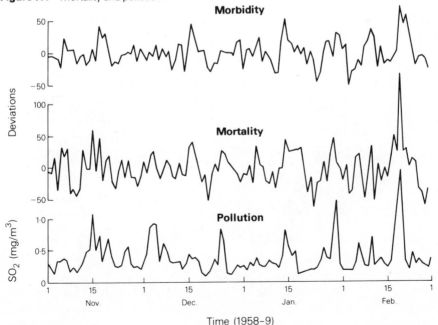

Time (1958-9)

The costs of air pollution and its control. As well as being a health hazard air pollution exacts an economic toll. Pollution corrodes metals, damages building surfaces and is injurious to vegetation and crops. Costs can be divided into two groups:

(a)   Direct – necessitating expenditure to repair pollution damage, for example blistering and disintegration of building stones, such as limestone; requiring structural repairs and cleaning of buildings; pollution soils household fabrics and decorations, and frequent laundering, cleaning and decorating is required.

(b)   Indirect – for example transport delays. Damage to agricultural, horticultural and ornamental plants in Greater Manchester at 1970 product sale prices probably exceeds £1 million of which about half probably arises from damage to grasslands.

It is naturally difficult to estimate the cost to the nation of air pollution but a figure of £350 millions per year was quoted as long ago as the late 1950s. Since then of course inflation and rises in the standard of living must have vastly increased this figure despite the savings achieved by pollution control. Fortunately few existing air pollutants are impossible to control, but the costs of purchasing, installing and running plant is often high, although sometimes the value of recovered materials can help to offset these costs. In the period 1958–68 about 0·2% of the Gross National Product was spent by industry installing

Figure 7.2   Sulphur dioxide pollution during the 1952 smog episode in London.

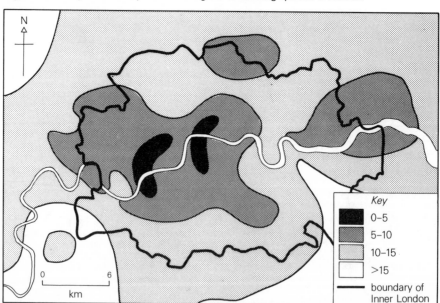

pollution control equipment. The Central Electricity Generating Board is the country's biggest single spender on control equipment.

Legislation to control air pollution was first enacted in Britain in 1306 during the reign of Edward I, when a law was passed prohibiting the burning of 'sea coal' because of its deleterious effects to health. Following the 1952 London smog disaster a committee led by Sir Hugh Beaver was set up and reported in 1954; their recommendations forming the basis of the parliamentary Clean Air Act in 1956. The objective of the Clean Air Act was to restrict emissions from domestic fires which were the major source of smoke pollution. Local authorities were encouraged to establish smoke control zones in which the burning of bituminous coal on domestic fires is prohibited. The costs of converting heating appliances to use smokeless fuels is shared between the government, the local authority and the householder. The larger, wealthier authorities have made most progress in setting up smoke control programmes, and while London, Yorkshire and parts of North West England have a good record, the areas covered by smoke control orders in South Wales, the East Midlands and parts of the North are still quite low. Opposition to the introduction of smokeless zones has come from the mining lobby, who traditionally receive an allowance of free or concessionary coal. Air pollution control legislation has been proposed and adopted by the European Community as part of its environmental action programme. Thornes (1979) has shown that the proposal directives which will be binding on member countries will represent a new departure for the UK, introducing air quality standards for the first time.

The Clean Air Act has been highly successful in reducing visible pollution, and average smoke concentrations have declined dramatically (by 80% since 1960). However changes in the pattern of industrial energy consumption as well as changes in domestic heating practices that would have occurred anyway, have helped to reduce smoke pollution and have made the Clean Air Act appear a much more successful piece of legislation than it is. High pollution episodes still occur, for example in mid-December 1975, smoke concentrations were up to 10 times as high as the winter average but they were less than one-sixth of the December 1962 levels. Medically undesirable 24-hour concentration levels of pollutants have been defined as 0.5 kgm^{-3} of sulphur dioxide, together with 0.25 kgm^{-3} of smoke. Although the emission of pollutants has been reduced in urban areas of the UK during the past two decades, given poor enough dispersal conditions over a sufficient time period, dangerous pollution concentrations may still be reached. Nevertheless the Clean Air Act has arguably been responsible for the biggest single improvement in the lives of Londoners in the last 25 years. Sulphur dioxide emissions have risen with electricity generating stations being largely responsible, but there has been a steady fall in average low-level concentrations of this gas in the UK. Continuing high concentrations of SO_2 in some urban areas, for example the City of London, has led to legislation prohibiting the burning of high sulphur fuels in such areas. The Central Electricity Generating Board has built taller chimneys at power stations and pollution is now spread over larger areas. Its life in the atmosphere is only a matter of days and much of it probably falls to earth as sulphate in rain. Sulphur dioxide has caused discolouration of leaves and premature leaf fall in forests near Port Talbot in South Wales, and many parts of the Pennines have been dismissed as potential areas for afforestation because of their exposure to SO_2 from Lancashire and the West Riding of Yorkshire. Monitoring of air pollution levels is clearly necessary and a national survey which began in 1962 is continuing. Measurements of smoke and SO_2 are made at over 1200 sampling sites in both urban and rural areas and the results are collected and processed by the government's Warren Springs Laboratory. This survey allows estimates of pollution within 5% accuracy on a national scale and within 10% on a regional scale.

Petrol engines emit poisons which include the gas carbon monoxide. Street concentrations are normally well below the danger level, but roadside measurements in central London have shown that very high concentrations can occur for short periods during occasions of congested slow-moving traffic. Ozone, a major component of photochemical air pollution, which can cause damage to crops, can occasionally in summer reach high levels of concentration in British cities. During the exceptional heatwave conditions of the summer of 1976 levels of ozone higher than the US air quality standard were measured, and typical of those on an average day in Los Angeles. We may conclude that under certain weather conditions some of the effects of mild photochemical smog do occur in Britain (Thornes 1977). Photochemical pollutants have been ignored in government legislation and since there is evidence that ozone can be imported from Europe as well as being generated within the UK any legislation must take into account air pollution transport across national boundaries.

With industries such as asbestos manufacture and brick-making the most serious pollutants come from the material of manufacture rather than the combustion fuels being used. The pungent objectionable smell spreading downwind from the chimneys of the Bedfordshire brickfields is unpleasant and also a hazard in so far as fluorine, one of the gases emitted, contaminates surrounding pastureland. Cattle eating contaminated fodder can suffer from fluorosis which leads to bone and teeth decay and eventual death of the animal. Asbestos particles represent a health hazard since inhalation of the fibres can lead to asbestosis, and prevention of the escape of particles to the atmosphere by industries handling asbestos must be strictly controlled. A consultant chest physician commenting on the incidence of asbestosis at Hebden Bridge, Yorkshire, pointed out that some residents developed lung damage simply by living for over 25 years to windward of a factory handling asbestos fibres.

Radioactive air pollution is perceived as a major hazard by large sections of the public, as evidenced by the length of the recently held inquiry into the siting of a radioactive waste reprocessing plant in Cumbria. The most serious reactor accident in the UK occurred in October 1957 at Windscale when fission products were released into the atmosphere and a downwind strip of land about 80 km long and 15 km wide was contaminated. Milk production from affected pastures had to cease.

Public perception of air pollution. The perception of pollution by the public and the degree of awareness and concern about it are likely to be important factors in determining the speed with which further pollution control measures are introduced. Surveys have been carried out in Sheffield, Edinburgh and Exeter (Burton *et al.* 1974) in the early 1970s. Reactions ranged from favourable in Sheffield where pressure groups existed working for cleaner air, to hostile in Exeter which was considered a healthy clean city where smoke control would result in unnecessary expenditure. The population of Sheffield has changed its perception of air pollution. While the city used to be thought of as smoky and dirty, dramatic improvements have occurred in smoke levels and an active publicity campaign claiming Sheffield to be 'the cleanest industrial city in Europe' has had a significant impact on the city's image. In general air pollution is not regarded as a serious problem by the public and there is little public anxiety about it, perhaps because the single most visible component of air pollution, smoke, has declined. There remains however a strong lobby, known originally as the Smoke Abatement Society, and now called the National Society for Clean Air, who have continued to press for higher air pollution standards through their journal *Clean air*. The Society has also initiated public education programmes.

Water pollution

River pollution occurs almost entirely as the result of effluent disposal and since the potential exists for typhoid, poliomyelitis and dysentry epidemics to be spread by water pollution, it is proper that we regard it as an environmental hazard. The Croydon typhoid epidemic of 1937 is thought to have been caused by sewage escaping along fissures in the chalk into a well from which drinking water was obtained. It is still a common and necessary practice for anyone unfortunate enough to fall into our most polluted rivers to be rushed to hospital to have their stomachs pumped out. Domestic sewage effluent is the most important source of water pollution. Many sewage works in the British Isles are either seriously overloaded or they are very old and hence do not produce a clean effluent. There are still many rivers which have middle and lower reaches where the oxygen content of the water is so low that the capacity of the river for self-purification is minimal and objectionable smells occur in the vicinity of the river. Between 1958 and 1970 the mileage of the most grossly polluted stretches of non-tidal rivers was reduced by 25% yet there are still about 3000 km of badly polluted stretches (Department of the Environment 1971). However, 86% of the rivers in England and Wales are now classified by the Department of the Environment in the top two classes of purity. In England and Wales control of water pollution is in the hands of the Regional Water Authorities whose responsibilities extend to all aspects of the water cycle. Pollution problems associated with agricultural wastes and especially runoff from areas dressed with nitrogen and phosphorous fertilisers and toxic pesticides occur in some parts of the country, and episodic fish kills have been caused by accidental discharges of such materials. Every discharge of polluted water has to be registered with and approved by one of the ten Water Authorities set up by the 1973 Water Act, and the Authority can specify the level of purity the proposed discharge must meet before consent is given. Seepage of hundreds of gallons of pesticides into the River Kyle in Yorkshire in early 1978 threatened to contaminate York's water supply. This incident highlighted the need for legislation to force farmers to store chemicals on farms in a safe manner. The 1974 Control of Pollution Act introduced the idea of water quality objectives. Instead of trying to raise all rivers to a pristine state a more pragmatic method was introduced with some rivers being allowed to continue to carry pollutants.

Water Authorities are required to supply a wholesome drinking water safe for human consumption, and as a guide to standards required use the data supplied by the World Health Organisation. The concentration of many trace substances in water supplies are kept under review. Recently it has been found that nitrate levels, often derived from intensive methods of agricultural husbandry, have been increasing. The toxic effects of nitrates are confined to the first few months of life and there have been occasions when it has been necessary to recommend the use of bottled water to make up infant feeds in some parts of East Anglia. Legislation is being drafted by the EEC to recommend a nitrate level below 25 mg per litre. In some London boroughs tap water contains about 40 mg per litre at present.

Figure 7.3   Water pollution in the Mersey estuary.

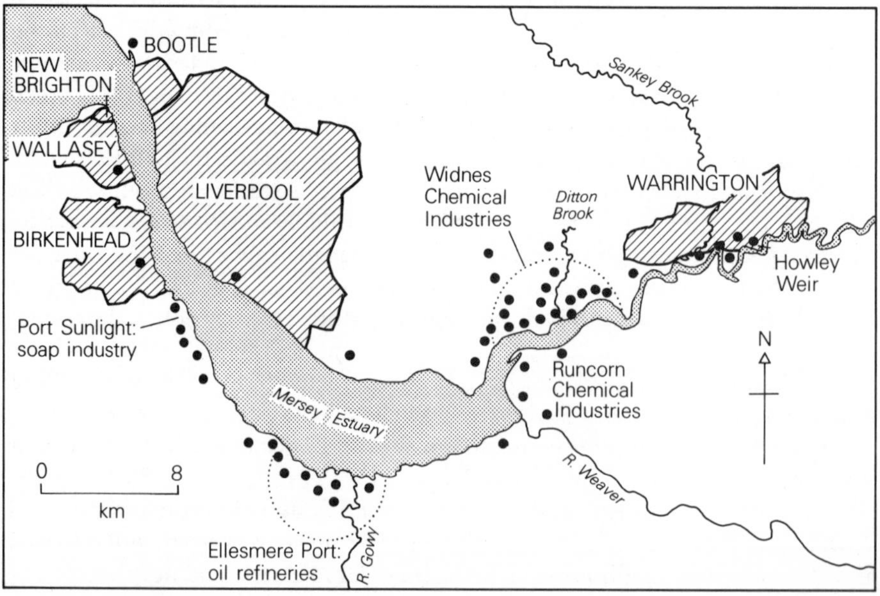

The most grievously polluted waters are those of the estuaries, and particularly the Tyne, Wear, Humber, Mersey and Severn. In many cases the level of pollution is sufficient to end the commercial use of shellfish, affect birds and sea mammals and restrict recreational use of nearby beaches (Royal Commission on Environmental Pollution 1972). About 8 million tons of sewage sludge are dumped annually in British coastal waters by 3 main authorities – London, Manchester and Glasgow. In a study of the Mersey, Bugler (1972) demonstrates how more than 50 industrial effluents contribute to pollution in the estuary (Fig. 7.3) and emphasised the enormous costs involved in cleaning up the river. Even where tidal rivers have been cleaned up, and the Thames provides a good example, the sea areas adjacent to the estuary mouth are often polluted by the dumping of sewage sludge and industrial waste. Significant quantities of heavy metals (about 200 tons per year in the Irish Sea alone), toxic chemicals and noxious waste are dumped each year and are undoubtedly to blame for such ecological disasters as the Seabird Wreck of 1969, when 100 000 seabirds died in the Irish Sea. The UK has signed the Oslo Convention under which we agree to transmit records to a central authority of the nature and quantities of substances dumped at sea in the North East Atlantic. The dispersion of pollutants in water tends to be slower than in the air, but there is a greater potential for bioaccumulation of persistent chemicals with an attendant risk to human health from contaminated fish and molluscs. The disposal of radioactive waste from nuclear power stations and plutonium plants poses a similar risk. Although the permissible levels for emissions into the Irish Sea are low, concern has been expressed for fisheries, and increased nuclear power generation will greatly exacerbate the problem of radioactive waste disposal.

Contamination of coastal bathing waters by untreated or only partially treated sewage has received a good deal of publicity in recent years. A survey along the South Wales coast (Edington & Edington 1977) which boasts a number of major holiday resorts, found sewage issuing directly on to some beaches from cracked and broken pipes. The bathing waters at 26 out of 45 beaches had a total coliform count exceeding the proposed EEC standard. Unfortunately interpreting the public health significance of such departures from recommended standards will

Figure 7.4 Major oil spills around the British coast.

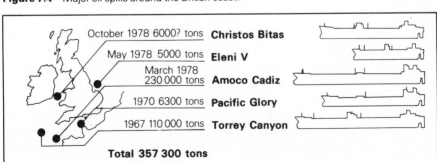

October 1978 6000? tons	**Christos Bitas**
May 1978 5000 tons	**Eleni V**
March 1978 230 000 tons	**Amoco Cadiz**
1970 6300 tons	**Pacific Glory**
1967 110 000 tons	**Torrey Canyon**

Total 357 300 tons

remain a problem until a comprehensive medical study is made of the likelihood of water-users contracting infections.

In recent years the greatest pollution threat to the coastline of the British Isles has been shown to come from oil spillages and oil tanker accidents in coastal waters. In March 1967 the Torrey Canyon, a super-tanker carrying crude oil, ran aground off the Cornish coast as a result of human error by the ship's master. As the tanks carrying the oil ruptured 110 000 tons of crude oil passed into the sea and soon began to contaminate 100 km of coastline in South West England (HMSO 1967). Not only were sea birds killed in great numbers but the strong detergents used to try to clean up the beaches proved highly destructive of marine life. In subsequent years a large number of oil slicks have contaminated parts of the coastline (Fig. 7.4). The Advisory Committee on Oil Pollution in the Sea (ACOPS) gives details of 595 incidents in 1976 and 642 in 1977 (see Fig. 7.5). Actions taken to attempt to combat the continued danger include the introduction of sea lanes in congested and restricted waterways handling large numbers of tankers, like the Straits of Dover, and onshore contingency plans have been made by coastal authorities to clean beaches using stockpiles of detergent cleaners. Incidents such as the collision of the Greek oil tanker Eleni V in May 1978 off the East Anglian coast with another vessel and the subsequent pollution of Norfolk and Suffolk holiday beaches following the inability to rapidly remove and destroy the wreck, raise a number of major issues which still require attention. It should be stressed that only 3–4% of the oil in the sea comes from accidents, five times as much comes from the routine flushing of ships' tanks. By far the greatest contributor to marine oil pollution is the land. Two-thirds of the oil in the sea comes from the land, washed down by the rivers.

Land pollution and industrial hazards

The pollution of land is generally localised in particular areas such as waste disposal tips; Britain is confronted with a rapidly growing problem of waste disposal, and in addition to domestic and trade refuse, complex chemical residues, often potentially toxic, are generated in increasing amounts by industry (Department of the Environment 1978). Groundwater resources can be polluted by percolating water from waste tips, although sand and gravel can be used as a natural filter. Tips have been known to pollute ground water for 80 years after all tipping has ceased. A survey of 1000 firms suggested about 1·8% of all industrial solid and semi-solid waste is toxic and most of this is disposed of by specialist contractors. The Deposit of Poisonous Wastes Act 1972 was passed as a step towards better control of such disposals and the legislation established a new offence – the disposal of wastes in a fashion that is likely to create an 'environmental hazard'. In recent years there have been examples of the irresponsible tipping of poisonous wastes creating a threat to public health, despite the severe penalties proposed in the Act. Following the death of a lorry driver at a toxic waste dump at Pitsea in Essex in 1975 due to the mixing of loads during dumping, a survey revealed 51 disposal sites which could be considered a risk to underground water supplies. Fires on such tips can result in poisonous fumes drifting across nearby residential areas as happened at a site in West Yorkshire in early 1978. A study of the disposal requirements of particular types of wastes has recently been published (Callely, Forster & Stafford 1979).

Figure 7.5   Oil pollution incidents during 1977.

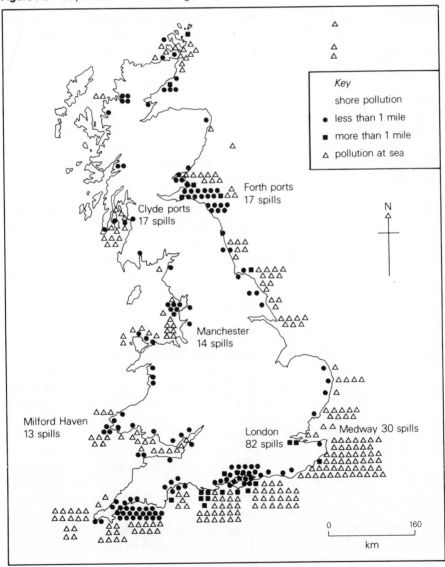

Following the Flixborough tragedy of June 1974 in south Humberside, increased concern has naturally been felt by people living close to industrial plants which handle or process materials which are highly inflammable, will easily explode or are highly toxic. This was Britain's largest ever peacetime explosion and killed 29 people, 27 of whom were employees of the Nypro works. Outside the plant more than 100 houses were destroyed or badly damaged and nearly 100 people were injured. Many plants are situated close to built-up areas and in places like Canvey Island, Essex, there are several potentially dangerous plants including oil refineries in close proximity to residential areas. Some islanders live with an oil storage depot, a cyclohexane depot (the chemical involved in the Flixborough explosion) and a natural gas treatment plant within a radius of 2 km of their homes. Figure 7.6 shows the distribution of major plants producing highly inflammable or explosive materials. There are between 4000 and 5000 plants in Britain which store dangerous chemicals which could lead to explosions and regulations are currently being drafted which will require companies to notify the government if they are processing toxic or flammable chemicals. In a report published in 1978 by the government's Health and Safety Executive, a hazard analysis was undertaken of the Canvey Island area and is the first comprehensive regional safety audit detailing risks faced by local inhabitants. The Canvey Islanders face an annual risk of accidental death caused by nearby industrial installations of 5 in 10 000. For comparison purposes the chances of accidental death from all causes averages 2·7 per 10 000 per year for 15–65 year-olds in Britain. Put another way it can be said that the inhabitants of the area face a higher risk than train drivers and coal miners face in their traditionally high-risk occupations. The report details theoretical studies of the worst possible accident which could occur and these suggest that more than half of the Island's 33 000 inhabitants would be killed. Suggestions have been made that a hazard inquiry should now be carried out in the Avonmouth area, where a variety of pharmaceutical fire retardant and aerosol products are made in factories close to a large housing estate.

Accidents to hazardous goods in transit by road or rail can lead to danger, particularly when corrosive chemicals are involved. In 1962 an explosion in West Bromwich followed a fire in a road tanker carrying chemicals which had been driven to a piece of waste land, 32 people were injured and there was considerable property damage, although the results could have been catastrophic if the accident had happened in a town centre. Unless emergency services know the exact nature of chemicals being carried and how they should be handled in the event of an accident the results can be disastrous. For example, hosing away a sodium leakage can set off a violent explosion. While travel on pre-arranged routes well clear of heavily populated areas and police escorts have been suggested as necessary, particularly after the disaster at Los Alfraques camp site on the Spanish Costa Blanca in July 1978, attention has focused on devising a clear, unambiguous labelling system for use on vehicles conveying chemicals. The HAZCHEM code has now been in use for 4 years and a CHEMSAFE code is also used. A tanker containing liquid petroleum gas if leaking presents a serious

Figure 7.6 Plants producing highly inflammable and explosive materials.

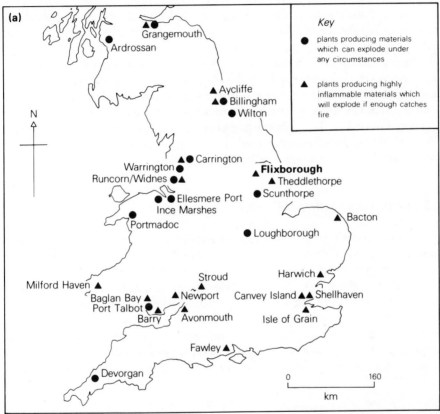

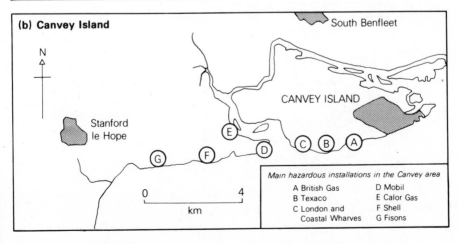

fire and explosion risk and toxic chemicals may require breathing apparatus and special clothing if they have to be handled. In Britain 1·5 million tons of the liquid petroleum gases, propane and butane, are moved every year as well as at least 40 million tons of chemicals, many of them toxic like chlorine and ammonia and 57 million tons of petroleum. In one incident in 1977, 2000 people were evacuated from central Glasgow when a fire threatened a 140 ton liquified–gas tank in a storage depot. The explosion in January 1979 in Bantry Bay, Ireland aboard a tanker using the oil terminal there, which resulted in 50 deaths, illustrates the risk run by communities who live close to points where tankers are operating in inshore waters. Loading and unloading operations can be particularly hazardous, and safety regulations at ports need to be continually revised. Tanker explosions can be checked by the use of inert gas systems designed to replace the explosive gases that gather above tanks filled with crude oil with non–explosive gases. Most large tankers now use such systems but many smaller vessels do not.

Heavy metal pollution

Maps of diseases reveal considerable variations in the distribution of the non-infectious ones and often there is no ready explanation, although the distinctive areal patterns are suggestive of environmental relationships. The biological implications of heavy metal contamination are presently unknown although many authorities now subscribe to the concept of sub–clinical metal poisoning leading to subtle derangements of the metabolism. An excellent review of trace element contamination has recently appeared (Purves 1977). Studies of the incidence of stomach cancer, multiple sclerosis, pernicious anaemia and other diseases suggest there is strong evidence for linking the presence of heavy metals

Figure 7.7   Heavy metal pollution at Avonmouth. The fall-out of lead and zinc around the smelter during a 21 day period in relation to wind direction.

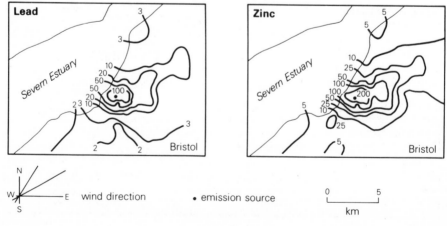

in soils with these diseases. Minerals such as cadmium and lead are toxic while copper and zinc, although essential for life processes, are toxic when present in excess. Upland Britain is characterised by old rocks, heavily mineralised with pockets of ores that have been mined and worked. Soils in the defunct metal mining districts, such as the Tamar Valley (Devon and Cornwall), and north Dyfed are very rich in these minerals, and although there is little visible environmental damage, relatively large amounts of toxic material enter the food chain and rural inhabitants of these areas can have higher blood concentrations, and more dental caries, than are common in other areas of geologically young rocks which are naturally low in metals such as cadmium, lead and zinc. Davies and Pinsent (1975) explain that 'it is unlikely that trace elements will prove to be the cause of any of the degenerative diseases, rather their significance may lie in altering the body's natural defence mechanisms to permit these diseases to progress'. Occasionally some rather dramatic evidence comes to light, for example in the village of Horrabridge in the Tamar Valley, three areas with contrasting cancer experience had three different water supplies, the worst part being served by well-water derived from mineralised strata (Allen-Price 1960).

It is accepted that the absorption of various heavy metals through the lung may be 3–10 times greater than through the gut, so that aerially-borne metals could be particularly significant. Geochemical reconnaissance maps for England and Wales have been produced by the Applied Geochemistry Research Group at Imperial College London (Thornton & Webb 1977, Applied Geochemistry Research Group 1977) and highlight areas of regional metal contamination by past and present-day industry. The trace metal content of river waters may at times exceed medical recommendations and it is important to have a knowledge of the upper limits that may be found at a potential extraction point. Detailed sampling in the soft water environment of South West England has demonstrated an encouraging degree of correlation between metals in sediments and waters, and served to confirm the thesis that a knowledge of the chemical composition of stream solutes can prove useful in the prediction of sites, where under certain conditions of rainfall and runoff, the metal load in associated waters may exceed recommended limits. The work of the Applied Geochemistry Research Group received a good deal of publicity early in 1979 when soil surveys found that a thousand villagers in Shipham, Somerset might be in danger from cadmium poisoning if locally grown food was consumed; much of the village having been built on cadmium-rich spoil tips from old mines. A programme of voluntary medical checks of the inhabitants was begun to ascertain the health risks involved. Soils developed on marine black shales in parts of South West England and Wales can be high in the trace element molybdenum which may be injurious to animal health, since the presence of the element depresses the availability of copper and this can cause deformation of bone structure.

Although high standards of pollution-arresting precautions are demanded in the vicinity of factories using and processing heavy metals a number of disquieting incidents have occurred. Blood lead levels of mothers and children living in the vicinity of a lead works in Tower Hamlets, East London were much higher than normal, while in 1972 the lead and zinc smelter at Avonmouth was closed for a time after dangerous lead levels were found in the blood of some of its workers and their families, as well as on vegetation near the smelter (see Fig. 7.7). Planning permission was refused for a new housing estate to have been built not far from the smelter. Livestock, and particularly horses, are very sensitive to heavy-metal poisoning and a number of fatalities have been reported from the Avonmouth area, the Lower Swansea Valley and from Derbyshire in recent years (Pattendon 1975). A survey of contamination and revegetation problems in the Lower Swansea Valley (Hilton 1967) found that toxic metals were concentrated in the soil at a level ten times higher in parts of the valley than in clean control regions in South Wales. Techniques have been developed for revegetating bare derelict land to eliminate the risk that exposed contaminated soils and smelter wastes might periodically dry out and be blown over a wide area of country constituting a health hazard to wildlife, crops and livestock (Goodman & Roberts 1971). The increasing use of sewage sludge on farmland which often contains concentrates of copper and lead can lead to contamination of land with these minerals.

Soft and acid water supplies can slowly corrode lead pipes and the overnight water in an area of old housing in Glasgow had ten times more lead content than in a group of younger houses (Addis & Moore 1974). Cardiovascular diseases and congenital malfunctions of the central nervous system seem to be more common in these areas of soft drinking water, and in a number of conurbations schemes are in hand now to speed up the removal of old lead piping from buildings. Water supplies are also treated chemically to reduce their plumbo-solvency where necessary.

The petrol engine is an important source of lead in the environment since organic lead is added as an anti-knock agent to petrol and this emerges in particle form in exhaust fumes contaminating soils in urban gardens, parks and allotments as well as near to motorways and main roads. One area where the potential for lead pollution from motor traffic has given rise to great concern is around the motorway interchange at Gravelly Hill near Birmingham ('Spaghetti Junction'). Currently about 1 million vehicles use the interchange each week and it has been calculated that about 9·5 kg of lead are discharged weekly within a radius of 0·5 km of the centre of the interchange. The on-going Birmingham blood level survey has been undertaken because of the concern generated about the high levels of lead in dust found in the city and a regular programme of sampling at frequent intervals is being undertaken. A research biologist at the Institute of Obstetrics and Gynaecology suggested that a marked rise in the birth rate in England and Wales in October and November 1977 might be attributed to a drop in the lead content of petrol following government controls imposed at the end of 1976. There remains a fear among many scientists that sub-clinical lead poisoning may be widespread although, following extensive investigations, the Department of the Environment (1974b) concluded that 'there is no evidence that the present levels of lead in the environment in general are an immediate hazard to human health'. The Joint Working Party on lead pollution around Gravelly Hill (Department of the Environment 1978b) reported that the degree of environmental contamination increased when the interchange opened, but is not markedly greater than elsewhere in Birmingham. However it was found that a relatively high proportion of pre-school children in the inner city areas have elevated blood level concentrations and further work is now required to investigate this problem fully. Some families living near London's urban motorway – Westway – are attempting to prosecute petrol companies and car manufacturers because their children have higher lead levels than is reckoned to be acceptable.

Noise pollution

One of the most important pollutants in contemporary urban areas is noise. Noise is unwanted sound, but it can be also thought of as wasted energy. Noise is one element of urban stress, which itself produces behavioural and physiological consequences. There is little reliable evidence of the connection between noise and mental illness, but noise does affect psychological reaction, and can lead to significant nervous strain. A group of doctors practising near London's Heathrow airport found that there was a higher rate of admission to psychiatric hospitals among people living in the area of maximum noise, although when the study was repeated using data for a later group of years the authors could not confirm the highly significant results shown in the original study.

The three major sources of noise in our society are:

(a)   industry (occupational noise polluting the environment),
(b)   transportation,
(c)   residential activities.

Noise has to be stopped at source or ameliorated at the reception site. With the recognition that noise is a pollutant technology in noise abatement is progressing. In the case of unwanted traffic noise, improved design, construction and location of urban motorways can reduce the disturbance to affected neighbourhoods. It has been found that the sensitivity of individuals to noise varies although generally the public is becoming increasingly aware of the noise problem, especially in cities.

The percentage of persons annoyed by aircraft noise varies with the level of exposure from 3–4% in quiet areas to 60–70% in the worst exposed areas. Noise levels beneath the flight path close to major airports can reach over 120 decibels and the government will give grants to householders in affected areas to reduce the noise levels in their homes. Significantly, only a small percentage of affected residents entitled to claim have done so, evidence perhaps that people adapt to incessant noise even though continuous exposure can lead to impaired hearing. Pressure by local communities reacting to aircraft noise has become an important feature in airport planning, and has necessitated the introduction of noise minimisation procedures, night curbs on flying and the routeing of aircraft approach away from residential areas. The noise hazard can lead to locational adjustments affecting for example house prices in an area. The arrival of supersonic flying has meant that annoyance from sonic booms affects large areas of the country.

While it is believed that about 2½ million residents suffer from severe aircraft noise, some 8 million people in the UK are affected by unacceptable levels of traffic noise. To help these sufferers, recent legislation has been designed to encourage noise abatement zones. Local authorities will have the power to fix target noise levels for various kinds of industrial premises. The idea of the zones was put forward in the Scott Report on Neighbourhood Noise prepared by the Noise Advisory Council, established in 1970. A two year experimental campaign to turn Darlington into the world's first 'quiet town' was conducted between 1976–8 and the results are now being evaluated. A curious outcome noted was that residents believed that noise in their neighbourhoods increased rather than diminished during the campaign, probably because they were made aware of noise pollution after a publicity drive that included the distribution of more than 100 000 leaflets – three to each house in the town.

The existing Noise Abatement Act of 1960 is a poor instrument for controlling industrial noise outside the factory wall since under the Act local authorities have little power to prevent noise occurring. They can only attempt to abate it once they are convinced a noise nuisance is occurring. Further legislation on noise emissions from individual road vehicles, the design of quieter equipment such as pneumatic drills, and a continuation of policies to separate traffic from pedestrians and town centres represent some of the ways in which the noise hazard can be contained.

Conclusions

While often patience is required in tackling old and persistent pollution problems, vigilance is needed in identifying new environmental threats. More knowledge is needed on a whole range of issues of which perhaps the major ones are:

(a)   The effects of long-term exposure to potentially harmful substances at concentrations which are not dangerous in the short term. The whole question of what constitutes an acceptable risk needs assessment, and this subject will be considered in more detail in Chapter 10.

(b)   The identification of substances which could be harmful if emitted into the environment. Studies to predict the behaviour of substances, perhaps from their chemical structures, are required.

(c)   The pathways of pollutants in the environment and the rate at which they are removed or destroyed.

Bibliography

Addis, G. and M. R. Moore 1974. Lead levels in the water of suburban Glasgow. *Nature* **252**, 120–1.

Allen-Price, E. D. 1960. Uneven distribution of cancer in West Devon with particular reference to the diverse water supply. *Lancet* **713**, 1235–8.

Applied Geochemistry Research Group 1977. *The Wolfson geochemical atlas of England and Wales*. Oxford: Clarendon Press.

Bach, W. 1972. *Atmospheric pollution*. New York: McGraw Hill.

Bugler, J. 1972. *Polluting Britain*. London: Penguin Books.

Burton, I. *et al.* 1974. Public response to a successful air pollution control programme. In *Climatic resources and economic activities,* J. Taylor (ed.), 173–91. Newton Abbot: David and Charles.

Callely, A. G., C. E. Forster and D. A. Stafford 1979. *Treatment of industrial effluent*. London: Hodder and Stoughton.

Charles, S. T. and K. J. Button 1976. Pollution, charges or standards? *Town and Country Planning* **44**, 29–31.

Coppock, J. T. and C. B. Wilson 1974. *Environmental quality*. Edinburgh: Scottish Academic Press.

Cresswell, C. R. 1974. *Notes on air pollution control*. London: H. K. Lewis and Co.

Davies, B. E. and J. E. H. Pinsent 1975. Minerals and morbidity. *Cambria* **2**, 85–93.

Department of the Environment 1971. *Report of a river pollution survey of England and Wales 1970*. London: HMSO, vol. 1.

Department of the Environment 1974a. *The monitoring of the environment in the UK*. Central Unit on Environ. Pollution. Pollut. Paper, no. 1. London: HMSO.

Department of the Environment 1974b. *Lead in the environment and its significance to man*. Central Unit on Environ. Pollution. Pollut. Paper, no. 2. London: HMSO.

Department of the Environment 1978a. *Hazardous wastes in landfill sites*. London: HMSO.

Department of the Environment 1978b. *Lead pollution in Birmingham*. Central Unit of Environ. Pollution. Pollut. Paper, no. 14. London: HMSO.

Edington, J. M. and M. A. Edington 1977. *Ecology and environmental planning*. London: Chapman and Hall.

Elsom, D. M. 1979. Air pollution episode in Greater Manchester. *Weather* **34**, 277–86.

Girt, J. L. 1972. Simple chronic bronchitis and urban ecological structure. In *Medical Geography,* N. D. McGlahan (ed.), 211–31. London: Methuen.

Goodman, G. T. and T. M. Roberts 1971. Plants and soils as indicators of metals in the air. *Nature* **231**, 287–92.

Health and Safety Executive 1978. *Canvey: an investigation of potential hazards from operations in the Canvey Island, Thurrock area*. London: HMSO.

Hilton, K. J. 1967. *The Lower Swansea Valley Project*. London: Longman.

HMSO 1967. *The Torrey Canyon. Report of the committee of scientists on scientific and technological aspects on the Torrey Canyon disaster*. London: HMSO.

HMSO 1978. *Fourth report of the select committee on science and technology 'Eleni V'*. London: HMSO.

Lawther, P. J. 1973. Air pollution and its effects on man. In *Pollution abatement,* K. M. Clayton (ed.), 39–60. Newton Abbot: David and Charles.

Little, P. and M. H. Martin 1974. Biological monitoring of heavy metal pollution. *Environ. Pollut.* **6**, 1–19.

Melvyn Howe, G. 1963. *National atlas of disease mortality in the UK*. London: Nelson.

Pattendon, N. J. 1975. *Report of a collaborative study of certain elements in air, soil, plants, animals and humans in the Swansea–Neath–Port Talbot area*. Cardiff: Welsh Office.

Phillip, A. E. 1974. Urban environments and mental health. In *Environmental quality*, Coppock, J. T. and C. B. Wilson (eds), 38–51. Edinburgh: Scottish Academic Press.

Purves, D. 1977. *Trace elements contamination of the environment*. London: Elsevier.

Rees, J. A. 1977. The economics of environmental management. *Geography* **62**, 311–24.

Royal Commission on Environmental Pollution 1972. *Pollution in some British estuaries and coastal waters*. London: HMSO. 3rd Report.

Thornes, J. E. 1977. Ozone comes to London. *Prog. Phys. Geog.* **1**, 506–17.

Thornes, J. E. 1979. The best practicable means of air quality management in the European Community. *Prog. Phys. Geog.* **3**, 427–42.

Thornton, I. and J. S. Webb 1970. Geochemical reconnaissance and the detection of trace element disorders in animals. In *Trace element metabolism in animals*, C. F. Mills (ed.). London: Livingstone Press.

Thornton, I. and J. S. Webb 1977. Application in the water industry of regional geochemical maps of England and Wales. *J. Inst. Water Engrs Scient.* **31**, 11–25.

Wall, G. 1976. National coping styles – policies to combat environmental problems. *Int. J. Environ. Studies* **9**, 239–45.

Waller, R. E. and B. T. Commins 1966. Episodes of high pollution in London 1952–66. *Int. Clean Air Congrss. Proc.* **1**, 228–31.

Wilkins, E. T. 1954. Air pollution aspects of the London fog of December 1952. *Q. J. R. Meteorol. Soc.* **80**, 267–82.

Wood, C. M. *et al.* 1974. *The geography of pollution – a study of greater Manchester*. Manchester: Manchester University Press.

8 *Seismic, geomorphological and pedological hazards*

'Soon or late the mountain falls
the rock moves from its place
water wears away the stones
the cloudburst erodes the soil.'
Job 14:18

The seismic hazard

Most people if asked would pronounce the British Isles to be fortunately free from the hazard of earthquakes. As Burton and Kates (1964) point out 'to the Englishman on his island, earthquakes are disasters that happen to others. It is recognised that while the ground is liable to open up at any moment beneath the feet of foreigners the English are safe because it can't happen here'. By the standards of those occurring along the San Andreas fault or the Japanese trench this is so, but earthquakes do occur from time to time and Davison (1924) listed no less than 1191 from the year AD 974 when, according to Symeon of Durham 'a great earthquake took place over all England', to 1924 when Hereford was affected by an earthquake for the twentieth time in 70 years.

With the building and proposed building of important sensitive structures such as nuclear power stations there is now a need for quantitative evaluation of the seismic hazard. Nuclear waste storage requires sites of great geological stability and although existing records imply that large quakes are rare in Britain the record is poor and incomplete. The return period of earthquakes leading to a rock movement of 1–2 cm at the surface is estimated to be about 50 years. Lilwall (1976) shows that many British cities are susceptible to an unpleasant amount of earthquake damage and although many tremors are quite small, a number reached intensity 8 on the 10 point Rossi–Forel scale and must be regarded as more than mere harmless curiosities. The largest intensity earthquake known in Britain occurred on 22 April 1884 and was centred near Colchester. Haining (1976) in his carefully researched account of the disaster, points out that its impact was experienced over a radius of 200 km and more than 1200 buildings were damaged. The village church at Langenhoe was wrecked. It

Figure 8.1 Epicentres of known earthquakes in Great Britain.

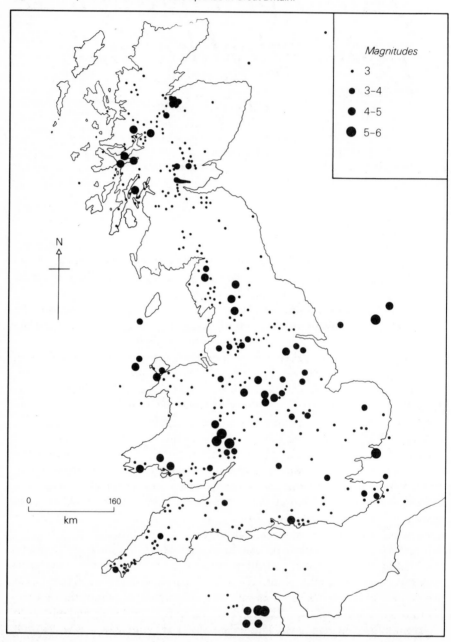

seems probable that the event caused the death of three people and the damage was so great that a disaster fund was set up to help to meet the repair costs. The earthquake must have been a considerable shock to the equanimity of the Victorians, but although it exceeded all others in terms of concentrated severity, the total disturbed area was far greater in the Hereford earthquake of 17 December 1896, when 218 chimneys were damaged.

From the plot of the epicentres of known earthquakes (Fig. 8.1) it can be seen that a diffuse area stretching from South Wales through Herefordshire into the North Midlands has had higher than average activity. Tremors of an intensity sufficient to break windows, crack weak plaster and masonry and cause damage to movable objects indoors have recurred quite frequently in this area. Elsewhere in Britain, the neighbourhoods of the Great Glen and Highland Boundary faults in Scotland, and Northern England, west of the Pennines, have been quite frequently affected. An earthquake with its epicentre near Carlisle caused damage in the latter area on Boxing Day 1979. Many of the larger events occur at depths of 30–60 km and most authorities agree that if the source of the tremors was nearer the surface widespread destruction would occur in a country of high population density. In the most prone areas small tremors occur very frequently, for example between 1970 and 1972 some two dozen small tremors occurred in Glenalmond, Perthshire, with epicentres in a very compact area near the village of Methven. Most earthquakes in the British Isles are associated with small movements along fault lines. Figure 8.2 shows the location of past events in the Lancashire region and the faulting pattern in the local Carboniferous rocks.

Figure 8.2 Past earthquakes and fault lines in Lancashire.

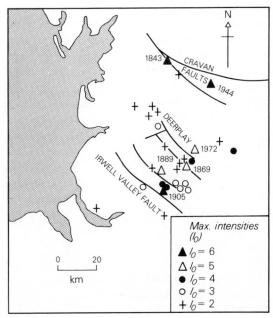

Lilwall (1976) notes that hazard assessment based purely on past seismicity can give erroneous results since apparent low risk zones may merely represent zones where strain is accumulating prior to release as an earthquake.

Small-scale tremors, the result of subsidence in mining areas are quite common. The Trent Vale area of North Staffordshire has suffered a plethora of tremors in recent years causing damage to property, which in places has reduced the value of some suburban housing. After about ten tremors early in 1975, the tremor on 15 July 1975 was felt over an area of 30 sq. km and caused damage to chimneys, plaster and brickwork. In the next two years 59 tremors were reported as felt by residents and microseismic surveys were carried out. The public were worried and uncertain about where to apply for compensation for damage suffered during the tremors, and although a hardship fund was set up and partly financed by the National Coal Board in August 1975, it was not until two years later that the NCB accepted liability and blame for the earth tremors and agreed to review future mining policy in North Staffordshire. Seismic surveys have revealed that the tremors, known locally as 'Goths' or 'Bumps' are attributable to an exceptional combination of geological and mining circumstances. Despite the considerable analysis undertaken however, the mechanism by which the tremors are produced is still largely unknown.

Minor earthquakes can be artificially induced through the filling of large reservoirs. Some 20 out of 270 with more than 100 m water depth have induced earthquakes and the construction of the new Craig Coch dam in mid-Wales will add to the list at risk.

Geomorphological hazards

The mass movement of land may produce hazardous situations, both inland, on occasions as a result of human actions, and on the coasts, primarily as a result of marine erosion. Situations susceptible to sudden mass movement include steep-sided valleys, steep hill slopes and scarps. While slow but inexorable movement over a long period of time is unlikely to produce serious trouble, it is the violent displacement under the action of gravity on an unstable slope that can produce movements, often referred to as landslides, which most frequently pose a hazard.

Landslides are clearly perceptible, down-slope soil or rock movements. Geotechnical research on landslides has been concerned mainly with understanding an event once it has happened, although more attention is now being paid by civil engineers and engineering geologists to the prediction of such events. There are sufficient high quality records of actual mass movements to support an understanding of the broader aspects of landsliding, although much progress remains to be made in elucidating the behaviour of soil and rock in the mass (NERC 1976). Little progress has been made on the prediction of failure or to the problem of landslide dynamics.

Cooke and Doornkamp (1974) suggest that landslides can be divided into three types:

(a)   Unpredicted slides causing immense damage and grief. The Aberfan disaster is the best example in the British Isles.
(b)   Slides which are known about, the threat and the need to control them being appreciated.
(c)   Slides which occur either along a proposed transport route or which potentially influence the site of a projected development.

Geomorphological mapping techniques making use of stereoscopic air photographs, conventional surveys and newer techniques such as space imagery can help to identify landslip-prone areas. Attention should be paid to old mass movements which could be reactivated, while the dating of past slides may involve historical surveys, radiocarbon methods and palynological techniques. New slides can occur because Man has the power to change the form of a hillside using modern technological developments. Areas are being used for civil engineering sites which are at best marginally suitable and which have previously been avoided while more favourable alternatives remained available. The instability of slopes, the interaction of factors involved and the actual behaviour of unstable areas can only be properly assessed by detailed evaluation of the properties of slope materials. Once the appropriate properties have been determined, stability calculations can be made (Prior 1978).

The forces promoting slope failure are complex. Shear-strength components such as the cohesion and frictional resistance of the material forming the slope, will be affected by water content and progressive geochemical and physical changes. Surface movement of landslides can be monitored by measuring the displacement of stakes related to fixed points, while sub-surface measurement can be obtained by instrumentation methods. Where field monitoring of processes proves difficult, laboratory simulation may provide complementary information. By pursuing techniques which may enable prediction of areas susceptible to landsliding and by identifying the controlling environmental characteristics of landslides, geomorphologists are contributing to the management of unstable areas.

If slopes which are potentially unstable can be identified this knowledge can be considered at the planning stage of an engineering project. In the case of a road route, alignment can avoid these slopes or if they must be crossed then remedial or controlling methods can be planned and costed. A good example of the results which can follow failure to pre-plan routes is offered by the Mam Tor stretch of the A625 road, built in 1802, between Manchester and Sheffield. The road runs alongside Mam Tor, known locally as the 'shivering mountain', and major collapses of the Carboniferous shales have occurred. The latest failure closed the road, which could only be reopened for light traffic in 1977 after £200 000 had been spent. It has been estimated that a new by-pass section will cost about £2½ millions to build. If new highway routes cross old landslips, deep cuttings can upset pre-existing critical equilibriums. The classic example of reactivation of relic landslide debris is the Walton's Wood slide in Staffordshire on the M6, where remedial work cost £600 000.

Any discussion of landslides must devote attention to the Aberfan disaster of 21 October, 1966 in South Wales. On this occasion a coal tip heap collapsed engulfing the Pantglas Infants' School, killing 147 people, 116 of whom were small children gathered in school for morning assembly. Aberfan lies on the floor of Taff Vale, and the tips of the Merthyr Vale Colliery overshadowed the village. Tip Seven consisted of a 67 m spoil heap of colliery waste material which had been allowed to accumulate on a steep hillside mostly above the 244 m contour in the years since 1958. About one-third of the material crashed on the village in a flow slide of 107 000 cubic metres travelling at between 16–32 km per hour. Following an earlier slip in 1963, concern in the village led to correspondence with the National Coal Board, but it was thought then that any future

Figure 8.3   Location of tip heaps and the village of Aberfan (after Waltham 1978).

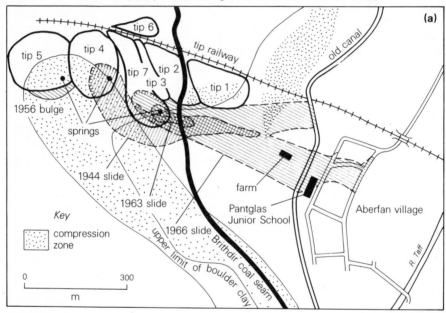

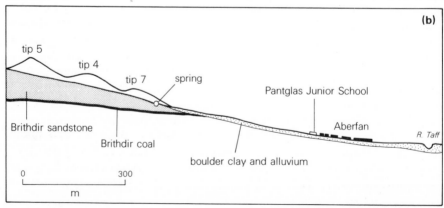

slippage would be slow enough for the village to be warned. The tribunal appointed to inquire into the disaster found that water percolating through the underlying Pennant sandstone issued as a spring beneath the lower part of the tip (Fig. 8.3, Miller 1974). This had led to removal of material from the toe of the tip, and following heavy rainfall the loose material comprising the tip became saturated making it susceptible to a catastrophic flow slide. The Tribunal of Inquiry under Lord Justice Edmund Davies reported that the 'Aberfan disaster could and should have been prevented' (HMSO 1967). There was a long history of previous tip slides in the area and the National Coal Board was reprimanded for its failure to devise and implement a safe tipping policy. The disaster focused attention on the remaining 1300 tips spread over South Wales. Many tip failures in South Wales (Knox 1927) have occurred, though not with such serious consequences, and tip inspection procedures have been revised and new draft codes of practice for spoil heaps introduced. Many of the South Wales valleys were settled during what appears to have been a relatively inactive period of mass movement and today find themselves threatened by what the Press refer to as 'moving mountains'. Some indication exists that rapid mass movement events are on the increase, perhaps because of increasing rainfall intensities. In 1968, in response to petitions from Aberfan residents the offending tip complex there was completely removed and work has also been carried out on landscaping, regrading and lowering other potentially dangerous tips in the area. Factors to be considered in assessing whether any major changes in the security of a tip might occur include ground water, tip geometry and alterations in the shear strength of the tipped material. Tip geometry may be affected by slow combustion taking place within the tip. The resultant burnt shale is friable and can easily be removed by heavy rainfall producing many hundreds of tons of black slurry which can flow downhill and flood into houses and on to the roads in the valley bottoms.

Torrential rain will often provide ideal conditions for mass movement and landslips. The 1952 Exmoor storm (see p. 72) allowed the West Lynn river to move more than 50 000 tons of boulders in a single day and stripped vegetation and soil from hillsides. Dozens of earth and debris landslips occurred in the Exe and neighbouring valleys draining Exmoor.

Rockslides and rockfalls occur where a steeply-sloping rock face is formed of a well jointed rock, such as is the case with many limestones. The Avon gorge at Bristol provides an example of a site where rockfalls can provide a hazard. Since 1974 the main road at the bottom of the gorge, known as the Portway, has been closed because of the threat from the near-vertical cliffs overshadowing it. These are formed of limestone with some interbedded mudstone layers, and much of the well jointed limestone has been further weakened by frost. Falls of large fragments could easily prove dangerous to road users below and a number of ideas have been investigated to stabilise the gorge sides. Bolts to hold the frost-shattered rock together and steel nets to encase the more dangerous sections were tried but it seems likely that it will be necessary to roof over the road with a protective gallery covered with soil and vegetation, so that falling rock fragments will not cause damage. At Dover differential weathering of chalk and flints in the cliffs above the town has caused concern and led in the mid–1960s to the cliffs being scaled to remove loose flints and lumps of fissured chalk which posed a hazard to houses in the vicinity. At Blaenau Ffestiniog, Gwynedd, a 50 m cliff overhangs property, shops and a chapel in the old slate quarrying town. Fears that the Bwlch y Gwynt rock face is unstable led to a survey by a firm of geological consultants who estimate it will cost more than £41 million to stabilise the face. No specific grants are available to meet the threat that exists and it seems likely that both the county council and the Welsh Office will have to provide funds.

Mudflows are an extremely important type of mass movement phenomena in which the dominant process is that of flow and they are particularly common on the coastal slopes of the eastern edge of the Antrim Plateau in Northern Ireland (Prior, Stephens & Douglas 1971). The breakdown of Liassic Shales to mud provides the bulk of the material involved in the mudflows in this area (see Fig. 8.4), which behave very erratically and which can, after heavy rainfall, move extremely rapidly (at more than 2·8 m per hour). The important Antrim coast road, constructed in the 19th century, is quite frequently blocked or damaged between Larne and Cushendell, disrupting traffic (see Figure 8.5). Rockfalls

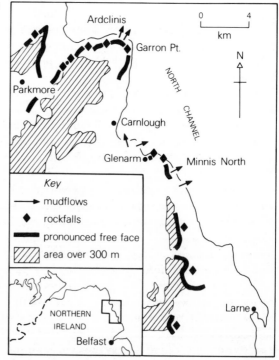

Figure 8.4 Location of mudflow and rockfall sites in C. Antrim.

from the chalk cliffs at Glenarm have necessitated the repositioning of the road away from the cliffs on an artificial embankment at one point, at considerable cost. Antrim County Council allocates a sum per annum for expenditure on slides and subsidences along the coast road. Subsidences and disalignments along the coast road stem from different causes. Near Garron Point the heavily loaded coastal slopes push downhill and the remains of five old road surfaces can be seen. Further south subsidences affecting the road are essentially the result of coastal erosion undermining the road bed.

The essential conditions for landslides, namely lack of support in front, and the development of a slip surface within the rock mass are met quite frequently at the coast. Along the south coast of England in particular; from Kent to Devon there are a number of locations where massive rocks like chalk overlie clay formations (e.g. Gault Clay) where slip planes can develop within or at the base of the clays. As a result of erosion at the cliff foot, massive rotational slips (i.e. turning about a horizontal axis) can occur. One such set of slips at Folkestone, where chalk overlies clays and Greensand, had a volume of 19 000 m³. Since 1844 this 4 km long unstable area has been crossed by the main Folkestone–Dover railway line and the coastal landslides here have probably been investigated

Figure 8.5 The Antrim coast road, N. Ireland, partially blocked by a rockfall. Both mudflows and rockfalls frequently disrupt traffic especially after periods of heavy rainfall.

more thoroughly than in any area of comparable size in the British Isles (Hutchinson 1969). Since the first recorded landslide in 1765 they have occurred at frequent intervals with major slips in 1915, 1937 and 1940. The massive movements in 1915 derailed a train and closed the railway for four years when the rail tracks were displaced by 10 m. The fundamental cause of the slips is the gradual erosion by the sea of the base of the 45 m thick Gault Clay which lies beneath 120 m of chalk. The great weight of the overlying chalk forces very plastic Gault Clay seawards, especially after heavy rain, extruding it like toothpaste on the foreshore. Drainage of the landslip and massive concrete toe weights built along the foreshore have decreased the number of movements in recent years. Further west, on the south coast of the Isle of Wight, huge landslides have caused damage, notably in March 1978, when property losses of £150 000 occurred as cottages, caravans, chalets and part of a holiday camp slipped. It was reported in the local daily newspaper that the area is so notorious for landslips that none of the properties was insurable for the risk. Clark (1978) has used the example of these Blackgang landslips to point out that the apparent paradox of investment being attracted to a zone of known hazardousness is in fact common and illustrates the low level of awareness of risk from natural hazards held by many decision-makers. The Dorset coast has a long history of landslide activity and coastal erosion resulting in the loss of agricultural land, damage to residential and industrial property and the development of unstable cliffs in a popular holiday area. In this area there has occurred some of the largest landslips in the British Isles (Arber 1973). On Christmas Eve 1839 at Downlands, east of Axmouth, a 3 km long cliff, 73 m in breadth and 45 m in depth moved nearly 60 m towards the sea. Cottages were destroyed and a new inland cliff was formed backing a chasm, 64 m deep and extending 800 m from east to west. Since no part of the Axmouth landslips can be considered secure ground, schemes which have been promoted for the development of holiday camps in the area seem particularly unsuitable.

Bog bursts leading to the downhill movement of masses of saturated peat can, for convenience, be included in this summary of landslide activity. They occur quite commonly in upland Ireland and in north-western counties of Britain. Many examples have been described in the Scientific Proceedings of the Royal Dublin Society, including the 1896 bog burst at Knocknageehan, Co. Kerry, which discharged 5×10^6 m of peat and is probably among the most severe occurrences on record. Bog flows, slides and bursts can poison fish in nearby rivers and cause damage to agricultural land. They frequently occur after periods of heavy rainfall when the surface layer of vegetation and peat becomes too weak to retain the semi-liquid mass of peat beneath. One of the most spectacular examples to have occurred in England affected Solway Moss, a hill 50 m high north of Carlisle in November 1771. On this occasion cattle and sheep were suffocated and large area of good agricultural land inundated by up to 6 m of mud and debris. Colhoun, Common and Cruickshank (1965) drew attention to bog flows in Co. Antrim in November 1963 which surged down the Glendun River wrecking a farmhouse and badly damaging farm equipment. Bog flows

Figure 8.6 Recorded bog flows in Ireland (after Colhoun, Common & Cruickshank 1965).

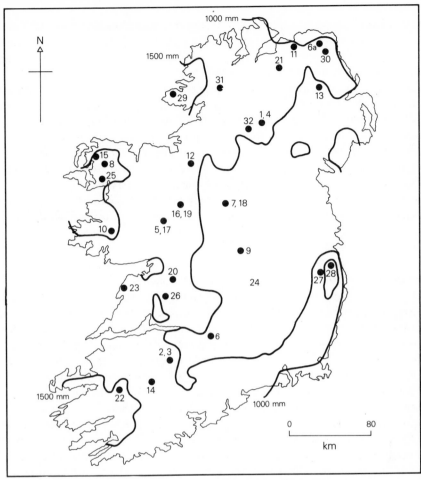

Key

1 before 1640, Clogher, Tyrone
2 1697, Charleville, Limerick, June
3 1708, Castlegarde, Limerick, January
4 1712, Clogher, Tyrone, March
5 1745, Dunmore, Galway, March, rain, cutting
6A 1788, Knocklayd, Antrim, May
6 1788, Dundrum, Tipperary, March
7 1809, Camlin valley, Longford, December, rain
8 1819, Owenmore valley, Erris, Mayo, January
9 1821, Clara Kings Co., June, cutting
10 1821, Joyce Country, Galway, September
11 1824, Ballywindelland, Derry, December
12 1832, Geevagh, Sligo, January, thaw
13 1835, Randalstown, Antrim, September
14 1840, Kanturk, Co. Cork, 1 January
15 1867, Glen Castle Hill, Belmullet, Mayo
16 1870, Castlereagh, Roscommon, December, cutting
17 1873, Dunmore, Galway, October, cutting

18 1883, Newtownforbes, Longford, January
19 1883, Castlereagh, Roscommon, January
20 1890, Slieve Aughty Mountains, Galway, January, thaw
21 1895, Dungiven, Derry, August, rain
22 1896, Killarney, Kerry, December, heavy rain, cutting
23 1900, Ballaghline, Clare, October
24 1906, Co. Offaly (locality uncertain), June, cutting
25 1931, Glencullin, Mayo, February, not heavy rain immediately before, no cutting
26 1934, Slieve Aughty Mountains, Clare, October, rain, no cutting
27 1937, Mullaghcleevaun, Wicklow, Spring, no cutting
28 1938, Powerscourt, Wicklow, July, rain, no cutting
29 1945, Glen valley, Donegal, January, rain and thaw, no cutting
30 1963, Cushendun, Antrim, November, rain, no cutting
31 1963, Barnesmore, Donegal, November, rain, cutting
32 1965, Slieve Rushen, Cavan, January, rain, and thaw

The occurrence of rain, snow thaw and turf cutting is noted only where it was recorded seem to have been more common in Ireland than elsewhere in the British Isles, and as can be seen in Figure 8.6 their distribution ranges throughout the island. In all cases where bursts in mountain bogs have been investigated there are indications that growth had rendered the bog unstable and the burst acted as a safety valve to restore equilibrium. Bursts, therefore may occupy a definite position in the cycle of development of bogs resting on sloping surfaces. As a result of heavy summer rainfall intensities, peat slides have been noted on Stainmore, Cumbria, on the North Yorkshire Moors and in Teesdale. The high retention of water by peat in summer may be due to cracking of the peat. This could contribute to a reduction in stability by encouraging higher soil porewater pressures, especially at the peat-bedrock interface.

In addition to landslides caused by the natural agents of denudation, there are numerous examples of ground surface subsidence, many of which have followed mining activities. Bell (1975) points out that with the exception of London and Merseyside, most of the large conurbations are located on coalfields, in some of which mining began centuries ago. Subsidence damage can necessitate the shoring up of houses as walls buckle and bulge. The bill for stabilisation work in the South Wales coalfield has become so large that local District Councils have campaigned for the setting up of a national disaster fund that local authorities could turn to in emergencies. The most common method of mitigating subsidence damage is by the introduction of flexibility in design following comprehensive site investigation before building commences. The total amount of subsidence can usually be reckoned as 90% of the thickness of a removed seam. Mining techniques such as leaving pillars of coal beneath areas which are to be built on can minimise subsidence. Although the extraction of coal is the major cause of subsidence in the UK it can be, and is, brought about by the removal of other substances from the ground. For example, salt has been worked in Cheshire for over 300 years (Waltham 1978). Extensive damage to houses and transport routes have occurred especially in the Dunkirk suburb of Northwich, partly as a result of uncontrolled extraction of the salt. A Brine Subsidence Compensation Board now deals with damage to land and buildings due to salt extraction and modern methods of controlled extraction have been introduced. The most severe phase of subsidence occurred between 1870 and 1920, but as Wallwork (1960) notes, although 'subsidence in its more violent forms is now rarely experienced, the cataclysmic upheavals of the 19th and early 20th centuries have given way to a more insidious form of subsidence which works stealthily to the same end – dereliction'. Subsidence damage on the saltfield has principally affected three types of land use:

(a)   Farmland. Subsidence has disturbed the water table with the formation of 'flashes', or subsidence lakes. Natural drainage systems have been impeded and in places flooding has become more frequent.
(b)   Communications and services. Damage has particularly affected the canal system in the Northwich area with roads and railways also affected from time to time.

(c) Buildings. Structural damage has been caused by subsidence. Ever since the onset of severe subsidence attempts have been made to construct frame buildings capable of resisting subsidence.

In parts of East Anglia shallow mining of chalk has been responsible for local subsidence. In July 1966 a row of houses at Bury St Edmunds, Suffolk was declared unsafe and had to be evacuated. Shallow holes or depressions with crater-like outlines caused by the collapse of underlying caverns are characteristic

Figure 8.7 The lost towns of East Yorkshire.

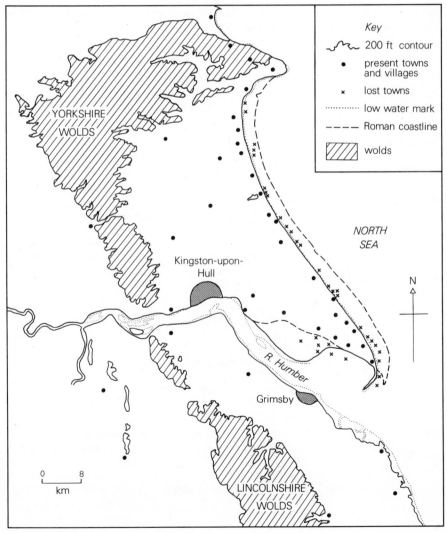

of areas underlain by calcareous beds. Many examples are found on the Carboniferous Limestone and Millstone Grit outcrops fringing the South Wales coalfield.

Along the coastline marine erosion is a serious natural hazard in many places, particularly on the east and south coasts of Britain. Steers (1953) and May (1977) have given good summaries of the extent of erosion and it is evident that over the centuries there has been a loss of hundreds of sq. km of land as a result of coastline recession. From a study of old maps and particularly the large scale Ordnance Survey maps, regions of heavy erosion can be traced. Along the Holderness coast of Yorkshire accurate measurements based on the position of the cliff face as shown on the OS map of 1852, and on subsequent editions right up to the present day, indicate a rate of erosion of between 1 and 6 m in places per annum (Valentin 1971). Not surprisingly many villages listed in the 1086 Domesday Survey have been swept away and in some cases even the name of the village has been lost as the whole parish has been consumed by the sea (Fig. 8.7). Between Mablethorpe and Skegness on the Lincolnshire coast five mediaeval parish churches have been lost to the sea. As with many other hazards both Man

Table 8.1 Causes of coastal erosion.

Types of erosion	Causal agents	
	Natural erosion	*Man-induced erosion*
accelerated destruction *(in situ)*	(1) increased wave energy (wind waves, storm surges, seiches, tsunamis) (2) frost action (cliffs) (3) ice scouring (4) wind action (dunes) (5) mass movements (landslips, slumping) (6) corrasion, corrosion, attrition and hydraulic action (rocky coasts) (7) marine fauna (8) floodwater (exiting through breached dunes) (9) changes in water levels (tectonic, isostatic and eustatic movements)	(1) beach excavation (2) offshore dredging (3) destruction of vegetation (or replacement with species having fewer sand retaining qualities) (4) permafrost melting (near Arctic oil fields)
beach starvation	(1) natural starvation (deep water offshore, submarine canyons) (2) null points (offshore foci from which sediment supply diverges) (3) natural inlets	(1) interception of littoral drift (groynes, jetties, 'improved' inlets) (2) arrest of supply at source (river dredging, dams, 'armoring' of headlands)

and nature make varying contributions to coastal erosion and this is illustrated in Table 8.1. A good example of man-induced erosion has occurred at Hallsands on the South Devon coast (see Fig. 8.8). At the turn of the century when extensions were being made to Devonport dockyard a local contractor was given permission by the Board of Trade to dredge shingle from the beach for use in concrete making. Altogether about ½ million ton was removed, despite local protests, and the beach lowered by about 5 m in places. Officials were convinced that the sea would replenish the beach shingle, but this did not happen, and during severe gales in 1917 the fishermen's cottages were destroyed and the hamlet had to be abandoned. Coastal geomorphologists believe that Hallsands beach was of great antiquity, perhaps being formed towards the end of the Ice Age, and when it was artificially removed the consequences were disastrous.

Along the east coast of England storm surges such as those of January 1953 can lead to periods of enhanced erosion. Clark (1978) has noted that rare but high-intensity events of this kind may come to dominate coastal environmental discussion and this can be misleading since many of the geomorphological changes experienced at the coast may represent not simply high-frequency but low-intensity events that do not reach hazard proportions. Nevertheless, the sandy cliffs in Suffolk near Covehithe south of Lowestoft retreated in places by 15–20 m as a result of the 1953 storm. Severe wave action undercut the cliffs which then collapsed on to the foreshore. A natural beach is an economic means

Figure 8.8 Man-induced coastal erosion at Hallsands, South Devon, in part the result of a lack of foresight as to what the consequences of removing shingle from the beach would be.

of absorbing the energy of breaking waves and so protecting an erodable coastline. The most severe erosion occurred where there were only narrow beaches. Concrete sea walls are one of the obvious protective devices against basal erosion of cliffs but their construction is expensive (£1 million a km is quite normal), and normally the cost can only be justified where property rather than agricultural or amenity land is threatened. This policy has resulted in coast protection works being carried out at Hornsea and Withernsea, on the Holderness coast, but the problem of erosion between the protected areas remains and the towns are in danger of becoming peninsulas. Sea walls can have a deleterious effect during storm conditions. This was demonstrated in 1953 when water overtopped the walls and washed out their foundations from behind, resulting, in several places, in their collapse and destruction. On the south coast at Bournemouth it has been noted that sea walls, primarily constructed to prevent further marine erosion of the cliffs, have created another problem in aiding the scouring of the beaches (May 1977). During stormy weather this process can be so marked that walls are undermined and damaged by high seas. Because of the necessity of maintaining good sandy beaches at this resort the authorities have engaged in a variety of measures to combat erosion ranging from the use of plastic seaweed to the tracing of sand movements by floats. Sea walls need to be designed on the basis of maximum probable wave height and on the importance of the structure to be protected.

The use of timber groynes is another traditional engineering approach to delay the longshore movement of sand and so help to build up a beach. The area downdrift of groynes can be starved of sand supply and subject therefore to enhanced erosion (Clayton 1977). This was a particularly difficult problem before the 1974 local government reorganisation produced larger authorities with responsibilities for coast defence. In fact, the whole coastal defence system has grown up in a piecemeal fashion often without the necessary research on the beach system which is the basis of its success or failure. Clark (1978) notes that major defence works 'often serve to satisfy public demand that something should be done'. Most coast defence schemes have been designed to protect a particular part of the coast and only rarely do they take account of adjacent sections. An interesting cost–benefit analysis of coastal erosion and various schemes to counteract it in East Anglia has been prepared by Simmonds (1977). An average cliff retreat of 1 m per year over 1 km length would mean 1000 sq. m per km per year are eroded. 1000 sq. metres of farmland valued at £2500 per hectare would be worth £250, but in the case of building land this figure could be as high as £60 000. The cost of a conventional coast protection scheme at a discounted capital cost of £1 million per km and lasting 25 years would be £40 000. The cost of an occasional catastrophic flood is put at £15 000 per km per year, a rather low figure perhaps because of the infrequency of such events. These figures take no account of the recreational value of the beach which Simmonds shows can be as high as £68 000 per km per year. Using these figures it can be seen in Table 8.1 that the 'do-nothing' approach may be justified in the case of threatened farmland, but with built-up land it would not pay to 'do nothing', and beach feeding with sand ought to be the choice on economic grounds. In fact, the artificial supply of sand to restore a deficiency caused by erosion is about the only coastal protection measure that does not adversely affect adjacent areas, and this beach nourishment is becoming an increasingly common approach to solve coastal erosion problems.

A good example of the social and economic consequences that can follow building in a hazardous situation is provided at Barton-on-Sea, Hampshire, and has been described by Clark (1974) and Clark, Ricketts and Small (1976). Here coastal recession affects local residents economically with the loss of individual properties in an area of high, and rising land values, as well as of open communal land. The central part of Christchurch Bay suffers from erosion partly through the incidence of high wave energy, but also as a result of local geology. There are two cliffs at Barton, one formed of Plateau Gravel and Barton Sand, which overlooks an undercliff of slumped material. The second cliff, formed of Barton Clay rises from beach level and underlies the undercliff (see Figs. 8.9 and 8.10). To counter erosion a two-fold policy of cliff-foot protection to encourage beach build up, and cliff-face works to intercept ground water bursting out from the undercliff, has been followed. A barrier of interlocking sheet piles are sunk through the undercliff into the Barton Clay to trap water behind the barrier which was then carried in drains to the sea (see Figure 8.11). Following a period of cliff stability from the mid-1960s public confidence in the efficiency of the works increased and some owners extended their cliff-top buildings. Major slips and erosion during 1974–5 destroyed considerable parts of the expensive protection scheme and highlighted the problems that can result if development right up to the coast is allowed in an active physical environment. Conflicts have developed involving various interest groups, including local residents, rate-payers and the District Council, and the community has shown itself to be divided as to strategy and tactics. The problems at Barton reflect ignorance as well as abuse of the coastal environment and the need for coastal management. In particular the use of a buffer strip of cliff top land which can absorb predicted erosion for the economic life of adjacent buildings and roads would be prudent. We need to remember that 'Britain is a living museum of the causes and effects of coastal erosion'.

Figure 8.9 Cliff profile at Barton-on-Sea, Hants.

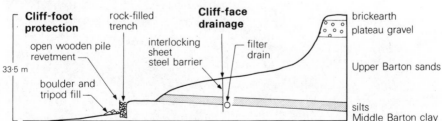

Figure 8.10   The lack of a management policy for these rapidly eroding cliffs at Barton-on-Sea, Hants has ensured that cliff-edge properties face imminent destruction despite attempts at cliff stabilisation.

Figure 8.11   Engineering works provide one costly attempt to overcome the problems of coastal erosion, but at Barton proved ineffective and a disamenity for beach users.

Loss and gain of land are going on constantly, and for some communities accretion may necessitate the adoption of new functions, as ports and harbours silt up. In the reign of Edward I, Harlech, Gwynedd, was a port while to day the castle lies well back from the sea. Blakeney and Cley in North Norfolk were flourishing ports in the 14th century when Norfolk exported wool to the Low Countries. In Sussex, Rye and Winchelsea were important ports before major silting took place in the Middle Ages behind the protective shingle ridges of Dungeness. At many ports of the present day dredging costs add to the total operating costs, but are essential if the port is to function. In excess of £10 millions is spent annually in dredging ports and harbours in Britain.

A very different type of coastal hazard is provided by the movement of coastal sand dunes. Dune coastlines are quite common in the British Isles, for example 20% of the Scottish Highlands coastline is fringed by sand dune accumulations, and there are important dune areas on the Lancashire coast north of Liverpool, the South Wales coast as well as in parts of West Wales and North Devon. Where there are no landward barriers, sand can encroach far inland burying both buildings and agricultural land. Literature and legend contain many references to disastrous sand drifts overwhelming churches and lands particularly during the storms of the late mediaeval period. Along the south shore of the Moray Firth between Nairn and Burghead the once flourishing fertile agricultural estate at Culbin House was inundated by sand during storms in 1694–5. The house, its associated cottages and the farmland had to be abandoned (Steers 1937), and today remains buried. An area of sand of 21 km^2 with individual dunes 30 m high now covers the area. To prevent further landward movement of the dunes, which already reach 5 km inland, afforestation with pine trees has been attempted, and elsewhere it is common practice to try to fix dunes with grasses such as Marram. Evidence for the movement of coastal dunes is provided by old records. Eccles church on the Norfolk coast was buried in 1839, but 23 years later the tower was uncovered as the dunes moved further inland.

Soil erosion – a pedological hazard

In 1945 Ward remarked that 'soil erosion is not a serious problem in this country'. Since then a survey of soil erosion suggests erosion is more widespread and occurs more frequently than was generally believed to be the case (Morgan 1975). Many erosion processes are accelerated by Man and soil erosion probably began with the clearance of the vegetation for agriculture by the first farmers about 5000 years ago. Erosion is as much related to conditions of crop and land management as it is to physical factors. Changing farming practices, including the elimination of grass fallows is exposing a larger proportion of the farm area to erosion. Removal of hedges and other protective barriers has increased field size sometimes facilitating erosion. One reason for the lack of concern about erosion is the almost complete absence of measurements of the rate at which it occurs.

Soil erosion by water may take the form of sheet erosion, rill erosion or gully erosion (see Figure 8.12). Erosion by water has been considered to be insignificant because of the low intensity of the rainfall but in 1975 Morgan noted significant erosion in counties as far apart as Kent, Devon, Bedfordshire and Cambridgeshire. In the latter county rill erosion was noted under well-established barley and grass crops. Erosion is normally worst on light sandy soils and often follows heavy summer thunderstorms. Morgan found that erosion rates on sandy soils in lowland England are high enough to give cause for concern, especially as they form 4% of the non-urban area of England and Wales, a total of 530 000 hectares. Fields subject to regular rilling produce lower yields, and crops are found to be more prone to disease. A spectacular example of gully erosion in a field on the Cromer Ridge in north Norfolk has been described by Evans and Nortcliff (1978). Gullies up to 2 m deep and 5 m wide could not be bridged by a combine harvester and a winter wheat crop had to be left uncut. Nearby erosion removed sugar beet and wheat plants leaving swathes of bare soil in the crops.

Degeneration of the vegetation cover by burning, overgrazing or recreational pressures often causes accelerated erosion on hillsides in upland Britain and gully erosion is frequent in such areas. The Peak District Joint Planning Board has recently initiated a research programme to try to find out why the present moorlands of Kinder, Bleaklow and Blackhill are heavily eroded. The loss of

Figure 8.12   Soil erosion by water in Britain can be destructive of agricultural land. Deep gullying in Norfolk illustrated here was produced by heavy downpours of rain.

Figure 8.13 Wind erosion of soils in Lincolnshire 1968 (after Robinson 1969).

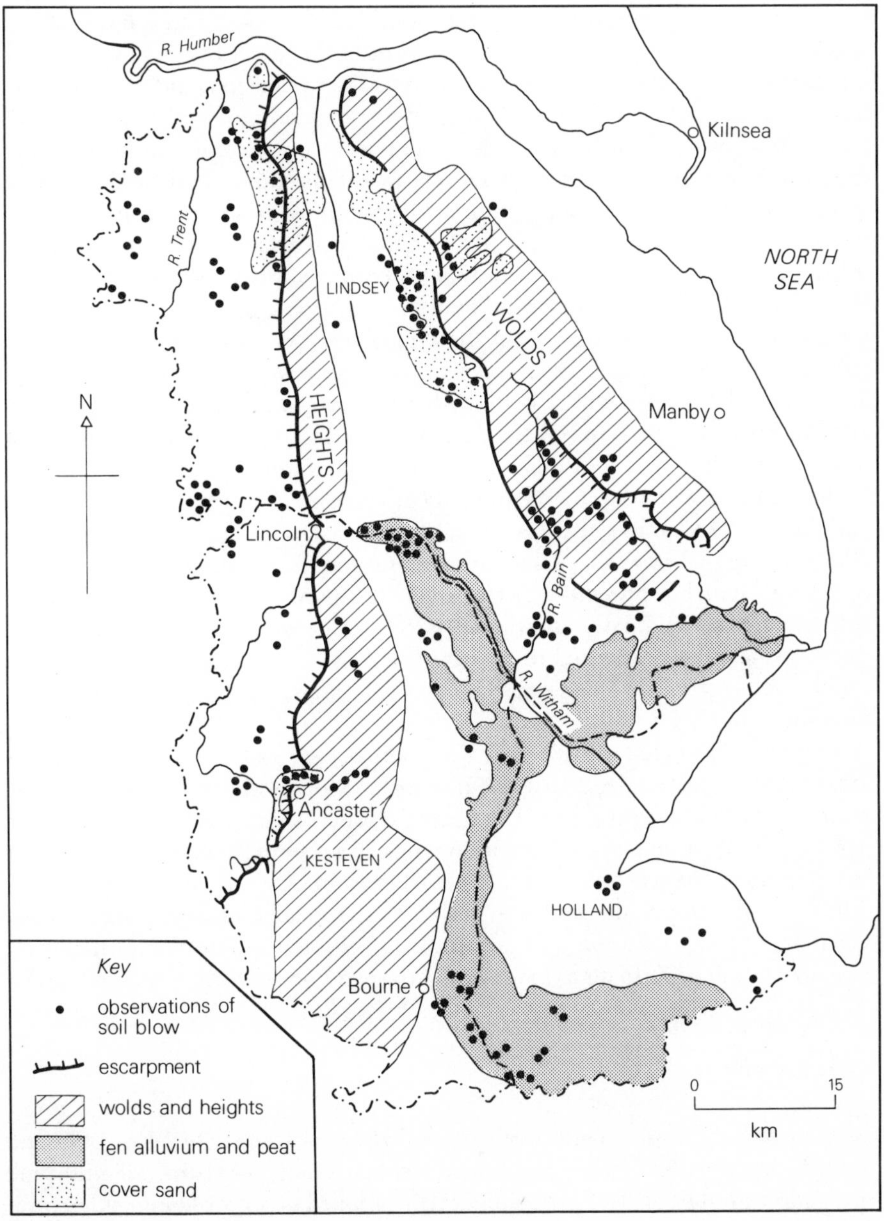

vegetation cover leads to poorer sheep grazing and less wildlife. Research based on sediment trap analysis has found very high rates of erosion in the area and the North West Water Authority believes that the Longendale reservoir's capacity has been reduced by 10% in the last 100 years. Published work on sediment accumulation rates in British reservoirs is sparse, and has generally relied on simple ground survey techniques, undertaken at low water conditions. Results suggest that British reservoirs are likely to be relatively efficient sediment traps. One survey in the Brecon Beacons showed that 80% of the area above 500 m showed some form of gullying. Eroded soils in the lower Swansea valley have resulted from vegetation removal by industrial air pollution, and deep gullying has affected about 200 ha and discouraged further plant growth (Bridges 1969).

The removal of soil by the wind is prevalent on the light soils of eastern England, especially the reclaimed fen peat and sandy soils of East Anglia. Strong winds can easily lift the top soil and fill the air with soil particles reducing visibility to a few metres, and in the Fens such occurrences are known as 'blows'. In the spring, before a continuous crop cover has been established, the soil clods when drying after rain, and tends to break up into small particles, which can easily be removed by the wind. In severe wind erosion episodes valuable top soil can be removed from the land and deposited in drainage channels and ditches. Dykes can fill with blown soil in as little as three hours and clearing them out can cost thousands of pounds. The danger of flooding exists if heavy rain falls before the drainage system can be restored to its normal state. A widespread blow in March 1968 partially blocked many roads, disrupting traffic and the cost of clearance was considerable, especially in Lincolnshire (Robinson 1969, see Fig. 8.13). Perhaps the most significant effect of soil erosion is the loss of topsoil, which represents an expensively fertilised and artificially productive substance essential to the continued good health of farming. A number of methods have been adopted to counter soil erosion, including the planting of shelter belts, strip cropping, marling and spraying with water at times when blowing is likely.

Morgan (1980) has shown that the incidence of soil erosion in Britain is localised in both time and space. Only certain storms give rise to erosion and only certain fields are affected. The potential for erosion (erosivity) is highest in parts of the Pennines, the Welsh mountains and the moorlands of the SW but how this potential is converted into actual erosion depends on the local conditions of soils, slope and land use as well as the quality of land management. Virtually nothing is known of the cost of erosion and until more information is available it will be difficult to make a case for spending more money on research.

Conclusions

Low frequency, high magnitude events that are characteristic of the climatic hazards described in section A are equally characteristic of seismic, geomorphic and pedological hazards. Fortunately, many applied geomorphologists are now aware of this and recently Brunsden and Thornes (1979) have remarked 'one of the most noticeable results of recent process studies is the increasing emphasis being placed on the role of extreme events on landform change'. In the crowded islands that comprise the British Isles there has often been pressure to take economic risks and to use land subject to mass movement in ways which can seem imprudent. In the USA the Colorado legislature has defined a geologic hazard as 'a phenomenon that is so adverse to past, current and foreseeable construction or land use as to constitute a significant hazard to public health and safety or to property'. Such a definition is applicable also in the British Isles as the many examples in this chapter reveal.

Bibliography

Arber, M. A. 1973. Landslips near Lyme Regis. *Proc. Geol. Assoc.* **84**, 121–33.

Bell, F. G. 1975. *Site investigation in areas of mining subsidence*. London: Newnes-Butterworth.

Bridges, E. M. 1969. Eroded soils in the lower Swansea valley. *J. Soil Sci.* **20**, 230–40.

Brunsden, D. and J. B. Thornes 1979. Landform evaluation. *Trans IBG* **4**, 463–84.

Burton, I. and R. W. Kates 1964. The perception of natural hazards. *Nat. Res. J.* **3**, 412–41.

Clark, M. J. 1974. Conflict on the coast. *Geography* **59**, 93–103.

Clark, M. J. 1978. Geomorphology in coastal zone environmental management. *Geography* **63**, 273–82.

Clark, M. J., P. J. Ricketts and R. J. Small 1976. Barton does not rule the waves. *Geogl Mag.* **49**, 622–5.

Clayton, K. 1977. Salvation from the sea. *Geogl Mag.* **59**, 622–5.

Colhoun, E. A., R. Common and M. A. Cruickshank 1965. Recent bog flows and debris slides in the North of Ireland. *Sci. Proc. R. Dublin Soc. A.* **2**, 163–74.

Cooke, R. U. and J. C. Doornkamp 1974. *Geomorphology in environmental management*. Oxford: Clarendon Press.

Davison, C. 1924. *A history of British earthquakes*. Cambridge: Cambridge University Press.

Evans, R. and S. Nortcliff 1978. Soil erosion in North Norfolk. *J. Agric. Sci.* **90**, 185–92.

Haining, P. 1976. *The great English earthquake*. London: Robert Hale.

HMSO 1967. *Report of the tribunal appointed to enquire into the disaster at Aberfan on 21 October 1966*. London: HMSO.

Hutchinson, J. N. 1969. A reconsideration of the coastal landslides at Folkestone Warren, Kent. *Geotechnique* **19**, 6–38.

Knox, G. 1927. Landslides in South Wales valleys. *Proc. S. Wales Inst. Engng* **43**, 161–280.

Lilwall, R. C. 1976. Seismicity and seismic hazard in Britain. *Seismological Bull.* **4**. London: Inst. Geol. Sci.

May, V. J. 1977. Earth cliffs. In *The coastline*, R. S. K. Barnes (ed.), 215–35. New York: John Wiley.

Miller, J. 1974. *Aberfan – a disaster and its aftermath*. London: Constable.

Morgan, R. P. C. 1975. Survey of soil erosion. *Geogl Mag.* **48**, 360–3.

Morgan, R. P. C. 1980. Soil erosion and conservation in Britain. *Prog. Phys. Geog.* **4**, 24–47.

NERC 1976. *Research on geomorphology of water-produced landforms.* Report of NERC Working Party, London Public. Series B.

Prior, D. B. 1978. Some recent progress and problems in the study of mass movement in Britain. In *Geomorphology: present problems and future prospects,* C. Embleton *et al.* (eds), Chapter 6, 84–106. Oxford: Oxford University Press.

Prior, D. B., N. Stephens and G. R. Douglas 1971. *Some examples of mudflows and rockfall activity in N.E. Ireland.* Special Public., **3**, 129–40. London: Inst. of Br. Geog.

Robinson, D. N. 1969. Soil erosion by wind in Lincolnshire March 1968. *East Midland Geographer* **30**, 351–61.

Simmonds, A. 1977. Benefits from beaches. *Geogl Mag.* **50**, 1–5.

Steers, J. A. 1937. The Culbin sands and Burghead Bay. *Geogl J.* **90**, 498–523.

Steers, J. A. 1953. *The sea coast.* New Naturalist Series. London: Collins.

Valentin, H. 1971. Land loss at Holderness. In *Applied coastal geomorphology,* J. A. Steers (ed.), 116–37. London: Macmillan.

Wallwork, K. L. 1960. Some problems of subsidence and land use in the mid–Cheshire industrial area. *Geogl J.* **126**, 191–9.

Waltham, T. 1978. *Catastrophe – the violent earth.* London: Macmillan.

Ward, W. H. 1945. The stability of natural slopes. *Geogl J.* **105**, 170–97.

9 Biological hazards

'Death rides on every passing breeze
He lurks in every flower
Each season has its own disease
Its peril every hour.'

Reginald Heber

Health hazards for Man

Disease can be conceptualised as maladaptation or lack of harmony in the environment with the response conditioned by the genetic make-up of the individual. The environment provides Man with his essential life-support system, but it also presents him with a variety of hazards which may prejudice his health (Melvyn Howe & Loraine 1973). Man cannot survive without the coexistence of a vast number of living micro-organisms, a small percentage of which are capable of producing human disease. Such micro-organisms are usually termed pathogens and many are essentially water-borne as can be seen in Table 9.1.

The economic and cultural changes of the last century have vastly improved living conditions in the British Isles, and since the discovery of antibiotics the population seems to have been lulled into a sense of false security regarding its susceptibility to infection. In the UK the number of working days lost as a result of virus infections far exceeds the number of days lost through strikes. It has been estimated that in one area of the city of Edinburgh no less than 7% of the population excrete some dysentry germs at any given moment of time. It is hardly surprising that given a less than adequate programme of sanitation and sewage disposal the spread of infection is all too likely if personal hygiene standards are lax.

Most disease is the result of some factor or factors in the environment. In western medicine, interest in short-term environmental changes and their effects on health can be traced back at least as far as Hippocrates, who wrote on the

Table 9.1   Diseases associated with water-borne pathogens.

Pathogen	Disease
algae	gastro-enteritis
bacteria	cholera, dysentery, typhoid
parasites	tapeworm
protozoa	dysentery
viruses	infectious hepatitis, poliomyelitis

subject in his *Airs, waters and places*. He noted 'if the winter be southerly, showery and mild, but the spring northerly dry and of a wintry character, the aged have catarrhs from their flabbiness and melting of the veins so that some of them die suddenly and some become paralytic on the right side or the left'. It has been estimated that over 80% of cancer, one of the major causes of death in the British Isles at the present time, is due primarily to some environmental factor. In view of the environmental dependence of disease, a search for the cause of a particular malady is in fact usually an attempt to identify the responsible factors in the environment. To this end the Medical Research Council operates an Environmental Hazards Unit at St Bartholomew's Hospital Medical College in London, while comprehensive analyses have been carried out of the distinctive geographical distributions of different diseases in the United Kingdom (Melvyn Howe 1963).

The relationship between weather, climate and disease constitutes the subject matter of the interdisciplinary science of biometeorology. Tromp (1963) has reviewed the considerable number of physiological changes that result from meteorological stresses and suggested that these may act as triggers in the case of some diseases. General resistance to infections may well be affected indirectly by the meteorological environment while there is evidence that the effect of drugs on patients can be influenced by weather and climate.

Improved sanitation, health legislation, education and medical advances have virtually eliminated such hazards as cholera, plague and smallpox which were rampant in the British Isles until as late as the early 20th century. Today we read with horror that 500 people died in ten days from cholera in Soho, London in 1848 as a result of polluted drinking water. In our own health-conscious times we tend to forget that the common housefly can carry 40 serious diseases, among them dysentry, and that rats, fleas and other pests continue to represent a hazard to Man. We also conveniently forget that even modern passenger jet aircraft allow their wash-basin water to be discharged into the atmosphere, while all waste from lavatories is disposed of by British Rail straight on to the track. With the removal from the scene of many killing infectious diseases, occasional epidemics of, for example, typhoid come as a shock and should act as a reminder that a breakdown in the system of control of water supplies, sewage or of private and public hygiene can quickly result in the spread of disease. The Aberdeen typhoid outbreak of May 1964 not only resulted in 150 confirmed cases of the disease, but led to a 50% drop in business in the city shops. An unpleasant side effect of rapid inter-continental travel is that potentially lethal diseases acquired abroad, which are not a public health risk in Britain, are becoming quite common here. Vigilance and a programme of improved health education among travellers is most necessary. One usually fatal disease which can easily be imported, but which fortunately has received wide publicity in recent years is rabies. Although widespread in many parts of Europe, British quarantine regulations for imported animals have prevented the disease from gaining a foothold in the British Isles and isolated occurrences have been contained.

One virus infection which retains the ability to inflict heavy casualties on vulnerable members of the population is influenza: 225 000 people died of it between September and November 1918. A series of worldwide epidemics (pandemics) have occurred this century and although effective vaccines can be prepared to give protection against known strains of the virus they are almost useless against new epidemics. Studies have been made of the spread of the disease (Hunter & Young 1971) during the 1957 epidemic (see Fig. 9.1) and the results suggest that some potential exists for prediction of the epidemic wave and this in turn may allow prophylactic measures to be concentrated in vulnerable areas in a future outbreak. In the UK sickness benefit claims during the Hong Kong influenza epidemic of 1969–70 cost over £30 millions in direct payment to insured persons and involved the loss of approximately 25 million working days in the period December 1969 to March 1970. The number of lost working days due to industrial disputes was approximately one-third of that number for the whole year. It is notable that influenza epidemics occur in the colder half of the year suggesting that climatological influences affect the disease, although this has not been clearly established. Macfarlane (1977) suggests that certain sequences of weather conditions with very low temperatures tend to

Figure 9.1   Influenza in England and Wales. Virus flow lines shown by weeks of epidemic onset (after Hunter & Young 1971).

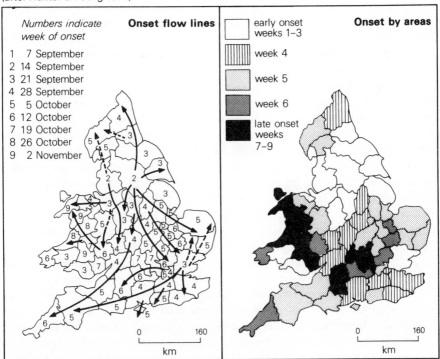

precede influenza epidemics given the presence of a strain of the virus to which the population is not yet immune. Complications among high risk groups of the population can result in high levels of mortality. More than 6000 influenza deaths in six months were noted during the 1957 outbreak.

Physiologists have looked closely at the effect of temperature on the body, but until the last decade very little interest was taken in the effect that humidity has on our bodies. With the vast increase in central heating, which in winter tends to dehumidify the air of both working places and domestic residences, this is becoming a much more important consideration. Before the environmental air can be used for gaseous exchange it has to be both humidified to almost saturation level and heated to the body temperature of 37°C. This is done efficiently in nasal breathing but, while breathing through the mouth, the enlarged surface area of the nose is lost and there is a much greater loss of heat and moisture from the lower respiratory tubes, which also have the role of preventing entry into the body of invading organisms. The Welsh National School of Medicine has been involved in a three year project survey in Sheffield to see if indoor working environments could be linked with the respiratory illnesses suffered by those exposed to the measured parameters. Positive correlations have been found and the overall trend is towards an increase in respiratory illnesses as the need for increased humidification and warming of inhaled air rises. This could well indicate that low indoor relative humidity may be a contributive factor in the occurrence of respiratory tract infections.

Melvyn Howe (1972) in a study of disease in Britain notes that the 'human response to environmental hazards is conditioned by the inborn constitution or genetic make-up of the individual'. Thus there will be varying degrees of adjustment or maladjustment to environmental hazards among different people throughout the country and susceptibility to infection and indeed the success of preventative medicine will vary greatly. Where people live in conditions of over-crowding, with poor household facilities and unsatisfactory diets, their liability to infection is normally much greater than when their living conditions and standards are better. Mortality experience over three times the UK average for tuberculosis, 60% in excess for lung cancer, 45% in excess for chronic bronchitis and a type of dysentry which has been called the 'Glasgow disease' because it is unique to the city, are some of the symptoms of the deep social malaise that has dogged Glasgow for 100 years. There is also evidence that the incidence of some important causes of mortality, for example Ischaemic heart disease may be at least partly linked to such factors as exposure to environmental stresses (Roberts & Lloyd 1972). A consistent and possibly causal relationship between cardiovascular disease and water hardness has been found in England and Wales and work is continuing to monitor the results of changes in the nature of water supply in particular areas (Crawford et al.1971).

Many people suffer much distress from their hypersensitivity to a wide variety of pollens and dusts which are present in the environment. At least half a million people suffer from severe 'hay fever' and related allergies. Small numbers of people also have allergies to insect stings, wasps for example caused 70 deaths in England and Wales between 1949–69. Some occupations have their own hazards. The inhalation of spores contained in mouldy hay can cause a pulmonary condition known as 'farmer's lung'.

Animal and plant hazards

Diseases which affect agricultural and horticultural crops can cause a reduction in yield which may be considerable in certain years and which means a financial loss both to the individual farmer and to the country as a whole. Sprays can be applied to combat some diseases but applications need to be kept to a minimum because of their high costs and long-term environmental effects. Research aimed at understanding the complex interaction between the plant and the attacking organism has enabled efficient forecasting schemes to be set up so that growers can be warned of the imminent arrival of a particular disease and can then institute appropriate action. Most of the widely distributed viruses are spread by insects such as aphids, and viruses are transmitted most efficiently under conditions suiting these vectors. Diseases in plants interfere with basic life processes such as photosynthesis and respiration and cause dysfunction in the flow and storage of food which may lead to the death of the plant. The resistance of trees to disease has been drastically reduced by pollution, modern forestry techniques and a massive use of herbicides. The recent rapid spread of Dutch elm disease, which is considered in detail below, illustrates that some diseases can gain a foothold even when individual specimens of the plant are geographically isolated from one another.

Under conditions of intensive agriculture disease can spread rapidly once established. Livestock farming involves a long-term capital input as herds are built up by careful breeding and financial compensation hardly recompenses a farmer who is forced to slaughter prize animals that are literally the outcome of a lifetime's work. Foot and mouth disease remains particularly feared since experience suggests that only by destroying infected animals can the disease be contained. Research work demonstrates the role of various environmental factors in spreading the disease and points the way to forecasting how an epidemic may spread.

An enormous increase in the numbers of some kind of living organism, whether it be an infectious virus, an aquatic weed or an animal can pose an environmental threat. Elton (1971) has studied these 'ecological explosions' and notes that the arrival and spread of myxomatosis amongst the rabbit population of the British Isles represents perhaps the biggest ecological explosion this century. The example of the aquatic weed *Sargassum muticum* is considered in some detail in this section to emphasise that new invaders continue to arrive, and can represent a hazard.

Dutch elm disease. The most serious tree epidemics have been triggered off by changes brought about to the biotic environment by the introduction of one or more alien parasites whose proliferation is not checked. For nearly 8000 years elms have been part of the landscape of the British Isles. During the 1960s and 1970s an aggressive strain of Dutch elm disease (so called because of its severity in the Netherlands in the 1930s), has killed more than 11 million trees and in many areas transformed the landscape making it poorer and barer. The tree formed a significant landscape element in many parts of the country, including the parks and gardens of towns and cities. A serious loss to the visual amenity of residents and tourists alike has been recorded in many places. It seems likely that it was under the bark of imported elm that beetles brought the fungus disease which has proved so destructive (Wilkinson 1977). The general spread of the disease has been tracked by Jones (1978). Southern England and the Midlands were affected in the early 1970s since when there has been a gradual spread of the disease northwards and westwards (Fig. 9.2) until by 1977 Dutch elm disease was being reported in the Dumfries and Galloway area of southern Scotland as well as in the Grampian region. It is possible that the mild winters of the early 1970s failed to kill beetles which might have been decimated in harder seasons, while the mid-1970s drought probably weakened the resistance of many trees and masked the symptoms of the disease in many others. Infected trees may take up to three years to die but few ever recover. Dead and dying trees provide breeding sites for a new generation of beetles which continue to spread the disease (Hedger 1979).

Under the Dutch Elm Disease (Local Authorities) Order 1974, county and regional authorities are empowered to serve compulsory felling notices on private landowners and a system of grants has been introduced to defray the cost of felling. Experience in southern England suggests that a programme of felling aimed at destroying the beetle's breeding and feeding sites can slow down the progress of the disease, but will not eradicate it. Only in a few instances have preventative measures managed to save some fine specimens of elm, particularly prized because of their influential effect on particular landscapes. Early in the spread of the disease the Forestry Commission recommended 'sanitation' felling in the hope that spread could be arrested but it is now believed that this policy is only workable where the elm population is geographically isolated or in an urban setting. The remaining 7½ million elms in southern England appear likely to succumb to the disease and local authorities have been urged to remove dead trees which otherwise could be a hazard in gales. It seems likely that over 90% of elms will be dead in southern England by the early 1980s.

Other specimens of trees in Britain are threatened by disease. Beech bark disease has been spreading in recent years while oak trees could quickly be affected if oak wilt disease were to be imported from North America. This century the tree population of the British Isles has declined considerably, with the diversity of tree species being reduced and ecologists have warned that unless foresters and plant pathologists work closely together we face the prospect of further massive reductions in the numbers of our deciduous trees.

Foot and mouth disease. Foot and mouth disease is a viral infection which affects cattle, pigs and sheep. The highly infectious virus is one of the smallest known

Figure 9.2 The spread of Dutch elm disease in Britain.

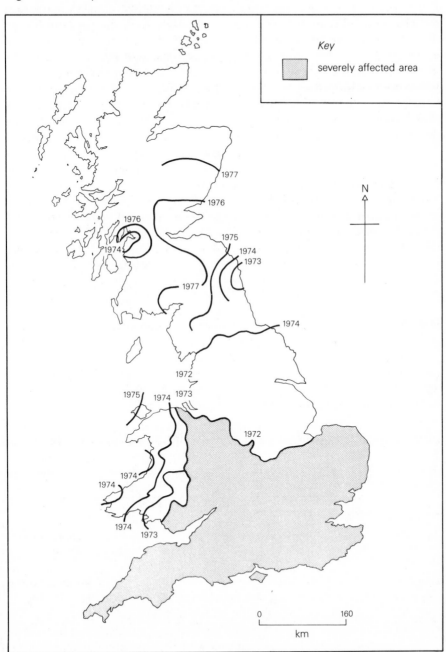

and an animal can become infected in one of three ways: inhalation, ingestion or direct contact with infected material. The approximate time scale for the development of the disease is shown in Figure 9.3. It is known that the disease can spread via 'famites', that is agents which do not themselves show symptoms. People or vehicles which come into contact with infected animals can transmit this disease to other animals. Vaccines are available for unaffected animals once the virus is identified but it takes 7 days before it becomes effective. It is economically advisable not to vaccinate as a standard practice because the number of outbreaks of the disease are fortunately small. Studies of the epidemic which infected more than 2300 farms in 1967–8, and caused large financial losses because animals had to be slaughtered, suggest that airborne spread plays a major part in the advance of the disease (Wright 1969). It appears likely that the disease often spreads through the effects of wind and precipitation. Continental sources frequently seem to be the initial source of the virus and primary outbreaks often occur near the east and south coasts of England. The virus must first get into the air in sufficient quantities to survive extensive dilution and it must then be transported and brought out of suspension, often by precipitation to contaminate grazing and fodder crops. Knowledge that wind may be a vital factor in spreading the disease should enable strict preventative measures to be taken on farms at risk during any future outbreaks of the disease in this country. Fodder exposed to the weather would have to be regarded as a potential risk, whether grazed directly or carried to housed animals.

Figure 9.3   Approximate time scale for development of foot and mouth disease.

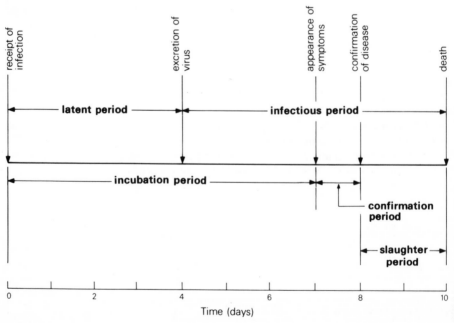

Water-borne botanical infestations. Manmade pollution has led some freshwater lakes in the British Isles to suffer the effects of algal blooms, which can have a detrimental effect on fish life as well as creating unpleasant smells and an unsightly appearance. Presho (1975) has described an algal bloom which affected Lough Neagh in Northern Ireland, the largest inland water-body in the British Isles. A eutrophication process took place in the lake, with the waters becoming richer in phosphorous and nitrogen, which promoted excessive algae growth. An estimated 350 tons of phosphates per year enter the lake, about 12 times the acceptable level, much of it arising from treated sewage effluent. If Lough Neagh experienced a long period of calm weather it could become oxygen-less and all life within it would die. Fortunately the lake lies in a windy environment, but from time to time algae concentrations can be blown into sheltered bays where the toxic effect of the dying blooms can harm fish life, for example eels in cages awaiting live shipment. Overabundance of algae causes increases in the midge population which feed on them and at certain times of the year these can be most irritating for lakeside residents and tourists enjoying the lake's amenities. Remedial measures which have been suggested to save the lake from dying include treatment works to remove the phosphate load from waters entering the lake. The Norfolk Broads represent a further example of water bodies suffering from the effects of eutrophication.

A giant Japanese seaweed, *Sargassum muticum* threatens to transform the intertidal coastal zone of southern England, fouling fishing lines and the propellors of small boats and affecting marinas. Gray and Gareth-Jones (1977) report that this brown seaweed was found in February 1973 in the Isle of Wight and has since spread as far west as Plymouth. The weed can grow at the rate of 1–2 cm per day and as it spreads can squeeze out other indigenous weeds. Early attempts by Man at eradicating the newcomer seem to have failed and it is probably now established permanently on the south coast.

Conclusions

The foregoing examples illustrate the heterogenous nature of biological hazards. Man, his crops and domestic animals are all at risk together with wildlife in general, while the quality of the environment can easily be impaired by the rapid spread of a new invader. The lifestyle of twentieth-century Man is often instrumental in allowing biological hazards to spread.

Bibliography

Crawford, M. D. *et al*. 1971. Changes in water hardness and local death rates. *Lancet* **2**, 327–34.
Elton, C. S. 1971. The invaders. In *Man's impact on environment*, T. R. Detwyler (ed.), 447–58. New York: McGraw Hill.

Gray, P. W. G. and E. B. Gareth-Jones 1977. The attempted clearance of *Sargassum muticum* from Britain. *Environ. Conserv.* **4**, 303–8.

Hedger, J. 1979. Has the elm a future? *The Ecologist* **9**, 131–5.

Hunter, J. M. and J. C. Young 1971. Diffusion of influenza in England and Wales. *Ann. Assoc. Am. Geogrs* **61**, 637–53.

Jones, P. 1978. Dutch elm disease moves north. *Geogl Mag.* **50**, 705–7.

Macfarlane, A. 1977. Daily mortality and environment in English conurbations: air pollution, low temperature and influenza in Greater London. *Br. J. Prevent. Soc. Med.* **31**, 54–61.

Melvyn Howe, G. 1963. *National atlas of disease mortality in the UK*. London: Thomas Nelson and Son.

Melvyn Howe, G. 1972. *Man, environment and disease in Britain*. Newton Abbot: David and Charles.

Melvyn Howe, G. and J. A. Loraine 1973. *Environmental medicine*. London: Heinemann Medical Books Ltd.

Presho, N. 1975. A dying lake. *Geogl Mag.* **48**, 8–14.

Roberts, C. J. and S. Lloyd 1972. Association between mortality from Ischaemic heart disease and rainfall in S. Wales and in the county boroughs of England and Wales. *Lancet* May 2, 1091–3.

Tromp, S. W. 1963. *Medical biometeorology*. London: Elsevier Publishing Co.

Wilkinson, G. 1977. *Epitaph for the elm*. London: Hutchinson.

Wright, P. B. 1969. Effect of wind and precipitation on the spread of foot and mouth disease. *Weather* **24**, 204–13.

10 *Vulnerability and risk*

'Be bold, be bold and everywhere be bold: but be not too bold.'
Edmund Spenser

Vulnerability

A consequence of adopting an approach which looks at the aggregate impact of hazards over the British Isles is that questions inevitably arise as to how vulnerable are different areas and sections of the population. Any analysis of vulnerability is extremely difficult because there is a degree of randomness inherent in damaging events which means that although we can identify, for example flood-prone areas, or areas at risk from gale force winds, pin-pointing where and when such hazardous events will occur is not possible. This randomness means that with our present knowledge of physical processes the more serious damaging events cannot be predicted with any precision. Trends in economic activities can easily result in changes in vulnerability. Thus the 'industrialisation' of agriculture has meant a diminished ability of farmers to deal with climatic hazards and the example has already been given in Chapter 3 of the increased vulnerability of this sector of the population to heavy snowfall.

Experimental integrations of the component distributions have been used to examine dimensions of individual hazards. Figure 10.1 gives an indication of drought impact in 1975–6 by combining information on agriculture, water supply, the incidence of fires and the occurrence of building foundation failures. The technique uses a 20×20 km square framework and a point score system. Pollutants have traditionally been studied individually but they unquestionably interact and vary spatially within large urban areas creating environments of strongly contrasting health risk. In an exploratory study Wood *et al.* (1974) aggregated six measures of pollution and calculated a composite pollution index for each of the 71 local authority areas in the Greater Manchester area. The pattern is mapped in Figure 10.2 and shows areas of high overall pollution around Salford in the centre of the conurbation and around Wigan in the west. The highest levels of pollution were generally found in areas with populations of low socio-economic status. Thus the derivation of a composite pollution index can highlight the disadvantaged areas and help in the formulation of pollution policies to be administered by local authorities.

The scope exists for employing these methods more widely to explore the regional ecology of damaging events. Attempts to consider the patterns of hazard proneness could involve investigations of two superimposed distributions. One distribution would represent the vulnerability to the range of environmental hazards described in this book. Over this distribution would then be superimposed a second one showing the concentrations of population and its social and economic variations together with qualitative data of the modes of community and administrative response to hazards. It could be expected that there would be both areas of coincidence and of dissimilarity

Figure 10.1   Drought impact in 1975–6.

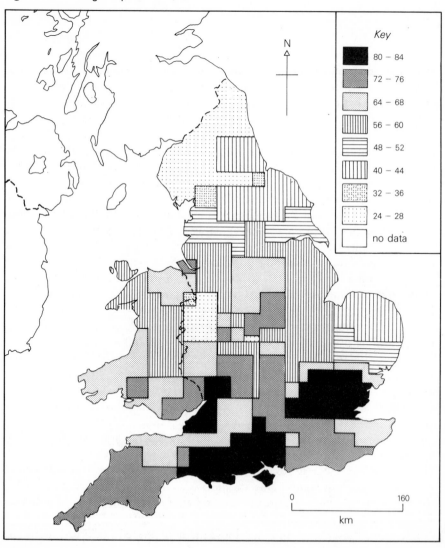

between these two distributions and the resultant combinations emerging from such an exercise could lead to a useful aetiology of vulnerability.

Risk assessment

Environmental hazards pose a risk of potential disaster. A disaster may occur as a result of the effect on human beings of the realisation of that risk. Previous chapters have shown that the consequences of hazardous events include threat to person, morbidity and mortality as well as damage to activities and wealth, both natural and manmade. While some environmental risks can be reasonably well anticipated, such as flooding in a valley or air pollution from an industrial smelter, others were wholly unsuspected effects at the time the technology or activity was developed. The effects of powerful agricultural chemicals in river systems are an example. Frequently they cause harm to people who have not voluntarily or specifically chosen to suffer their consequences and thus they

Figure 10.2   Pollution index in the Greater Manchester area.

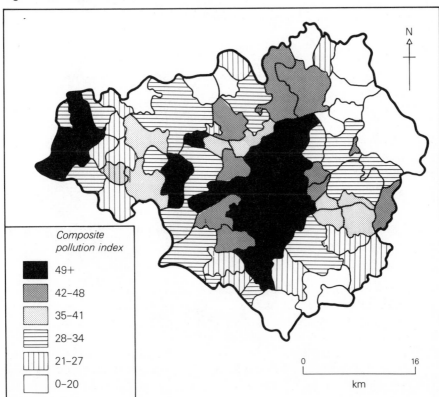

Composite
pollution index

■ 49+

▓ 42–48

░ 35–41

≣ 28–34

▥ 21–27

□ 0–20

0   16

km

require regulation on the part of some authority above that of an individual citizen (Burton & Whyte 1980). They are characteristically multi-dimensional problems which cut across the normal jurisdiction of government departments. In the United Kingdom the chief risk management authority, the Health and Safety Executive is linked to Parliament through three ministeries – Employment, Environment and Industry.

The assessment of the threat potential of hazards is essential if we are to try to achieve a sense of proportion about the environmental hazards we face. It is clear that the public feels a greater shock from an infrequent catastrophe, such as the 1952 Lynmouth floods, or the Aberfan disaster, in which several deaths occur, than it does from the same number of persons dying in ones and twos on frequent occasions, for example in road accidents. It is illuminating to compare the reaction to the Aberfan incident with the much greater, but relatively random death toll accepted by road users. When disasters, minor in terms of loss of life anyway, occur in the British Isles there is always a great surge of indignation, yet the perpetual carnage on the roads generates no public outrage. One reason for this is undoubtedly the speed and ubiquity with which information about disasters is disseminated and the endless comment and analysis of them that follows in the media. Clearly then a distinction can be made between 'routine hazards', characterised by well defined risks and consequences and 'catastrophic hazards' with poorly defined risks.

Risk assessment involves:

(a) Risk identification – the recognition that a hazard with definable characteristics exists.
(b) Risk estimation – the scientific determination of the nature and level of the risk.
(c) Risk evaluation – judgements about the significance and acceptability of risk probabilities and consequences.
(d) Risk control – the choice and implementation of intervention or the decision not to intervene.

A variety of methods of risk estimation are available of which two of the most commonly used are:

(a) Extrapolation from experience. Past events are projected into the future in order to estimate the likelihood of events or rates of continuance of observed trends. Estimates of the changes that may occur in atmospheric composition serve as an example.
(b) The analogue method. Experience is transferred from a different but not dissimilar situation, for example estimates of the maximum probable flood in a small river basin with poor records may be achieved by transferring known weather patterns of the region into that basin.

Figure 10.3   A comparison of hazard levels.

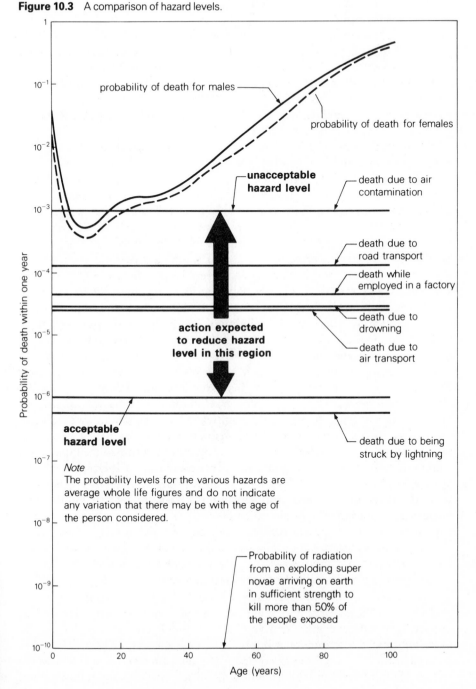

Assessment of risk demands a scientific understanding and a social judgement as to which risks to accept, which to reduce and when to forgo or limit the use of a technology or natural location (Hohenemser & Kates 1978).

A complete comparison of the significance of particular hazards would involve comparisons of financial loss, injury and death and would be extremely difficult. Most analyses of risk estimation have taken the statistics of death rates only as a reasonable index of the harm of different hazards. Human death is the best defined of all hazard consequences. Kates (1978) suggests that natural disasters tend to set a base guide for risk. If the probability of a hazard is small compared with natural hazards it will be considered to be acceptable. Chicken (1975) has compared the probability of normal death (based on life expectancy tables) with the risk of death from various manmade hazards and from such natural hazards as drowning or being struck by lightning. From Figure 10.3 it is possible to infer that unacceptable hazards are those which have a probability of causing death within a year greater than 10^{-3}, acceptable hazards are those with a probability of death within a year of less than 10^{-6}, and if the hazard has a probability of between 10^{-3} and 10^{-6}, then it is to be expected that steps will be taken to reduce the hazard to an acceptable level. In fact analysis of this kind can be highly misleading because it does not differentiate between death risks that are incurred voluntarily, like taking contraceptive pills (one in 50 000 women killed per year), or those that are involuntary, like dying from influenza (one in 18 000 die per year). In the context of Figure 10.3 it could be argued that the risk of being killed by being struck by lightning can be lessened by taking simple precautions, like staying indoors during thunderstorms. By contrast, since a human being cannot stop breathing, the risk of death due to air contamination cannot so easily be reduced. The risk of being killed in a car accident in Great Britain is about one in 7500 per year. Any individual can, however, substantially alter his own personal risk by driving carefully in a well maintained car, not drinking and abiding strictly by the Highway Code. The idea of an 'Index of risks' with all risks expressed as one in so many thousands is a dangerous simplification of a complex issue. No one figure can encompass all the varied factors that enter into risk assessment. In his controversial Richard Dimbleby lecture, Lord Rothschild (1978) sought to show that uranium-power generation was one of the safest sources of energy. His critics argued that the risk of a nuclear power accident was almost impossible to assess given that so far our experience of nuclear power is limited in both time and number of plants and that the event we fear has not yet happened. For the present anyway, the nuclear lobby can assert that 'there is not a single tombstone standing over any grave in this country as a result of the British nuclear industry'.

Hazards arising explicitly or implicitly out of technological practices in industrialised areas like the British Isles, have significantly surpassed natural hazards in impact, cost and general importance. Man is not only creating new hazards by modifying the environment but is forcing new people and old hazards together in fresh areas. Increased media coverage of environmental hazards has been a feature of recent years and this has included much speculation about the kind and scale of hazards which might affect us in the future. Although scientific research and press coverage has increased, this has not made it any easier to find a perspective among the bewildering array of environmental threats having catastrophic potential. The containment of some hazards rests largely in our own hands. If we are to prevent rabies from becoming endemic in the British Isles, or virus diseases like smallpox escaping from research units, we have not merely to be vigilant, but create the necessary legal and administrative apparatus to ensure our own protection. The dramatic increase in the scale of the communication media leads to exaggerated assessment, and creates the illusion of threat from what may be highly localised problems. The recent concern about microwave radiation emanating from satellite tracking stations, powerful radar systems and military installations is a good example. If risks are overassessed, resources may be squandered in their abatement, while if they are underassessed the hazard remains to imperil human life.

A most challenging aspect of hazard research lies in estimating hazards not yet experienced. Rare and unexpected events take on a particular significance. The example of the chemical plant explosion at Flixborough illustrates how one accident can completely change the risk assessment by making an 'incredible' event only too credible. Flixborough has been described as the single most important event in forming British public opinion about industrial hazards since the Second World War (McGinty 1976). No risk assessment was made for the event and thus no judgement made on its acceptability, either in consequence or probability terms. A very different situation existed in the UK for major chemical plants compared to the detailed risk assessment and stringent regulations imposed on nuclear power stations. For the future, hazard identification will depend for the most part on scientific research, screening, monitoring and diagnosis. By far the most serious problem is the unknown hazard. It appears likely that our complex, technological society, especially in the heavily urbanised and industrialised areas is increasingly subject to unknown or poorly defined risks, the likelihood of which is probably very low, but which can in fact scarcely be guessed at, let alone estimated.

Bibliography

Burton, I. and A. V. Whyte 1980. *Environmental risk management*. Scope Report 14. New York: John Wiley.

Chicken, J. C. 1975. *Hazard control policy in Britain*. London: Pergamon Press.

Hohenemser, C. and R. W. Kates 1978. Our hazardous environment. *Environment* **20**, 6–41.

Kates, R. W. 1978. *Risk assessment of environmental hazards*. Scope Report 8. New York: John Wiley.

McGinty, L. 1976. Whose acceptable risk? *New Scientist* **72**, 16 Sept. 582–3.

Rothschild, Lord 1978. Risk. *The Listener* **100**, 715–8.

Wood, C. M. *et al.* 1974. *The geography of pollution – a study of Greater Manchester*. Manchester: Manchester University Press.

Index